The American Point System

Origin Of

The American Point System

For Printers' Type Measurement

By

Richard L. Hopkins

HILL & DALE PRESS

Terra Alta, West Virginia

Printed in the United States of America

DEDICATED
TO A MOST UNDERSTANDING WIFE
LYNDA

Forward

Metrication—converting our traditional measures of inches, feet, miles and others—is being vigorously pursued today both in England and the United States. The U. S. Commerce Department has recommended that metric measures be adopted through a "coordinated national program." The British already are implementing the system.

The British have developed a plan for measuring type in metrics and although they don't plan to adopt it anytime soon, the drive for metrication obviously signals the eventual abandonment of the present point system for type measurement.

For years the point system has been the standard for English-speaking printers the world over. It seems to be such an established fact to most printers—like the multiplication table. We do not think of it as of very recent origin, nor do we think of it as the result of one man's effort. Nelson C. Hawks, originator of the American (and British) system, already has passed into obscurity, denied his very special position in the annals of printing history.

Before his point system also falls into obscurity, the full story of its origin, spread, and final acceptance as an international standard should be told. So here it is.

Inspiration and Help

There always must be a beginning. Mine was with the gift of a near-complete file of the *Inland Printer* from 1885 to 1902. That gift, on the part of Dr. Quintus C. Wilson, dean emeritus of the West Virginia University School of Journalism, whetted my appetite for details of early printing activities in this country. The file has provided invaluable and readily accessible source material to me and for this gift, I will always remain grateful.

The West Virginia University Faculty Senate Committee for Research Grants also should be recognized, for a grant from this committee made travel to various libraries possible. This research never could have been made without such financial assistance.

The Houghton Libarary at Harvard University, and the American Type Founders Library, now housed in the Butler Library at Columbia University, must be recognized for providing much resource material.

Most valuable, however, were the resources and personal assistance provided by Mr. George L. Harding, honorary curator of the Edward C. Kemble Collections on American Printing and Publishing, at the California Historical Society in San Francisco.

Mr. Harding himself is responsible for gathering most of the documents now preserved in the Kemble Collection pertaining to Nelson C. Hawks. Many of these were obtained in the years immediately following Hawks' death at Alameda, California, in 1929.

Richard L. Hopkins
April, 1975

Contents

List of Illustrations

Chapter One

The Evolution of Type Sizes

THE RELATIVE SIZE of type did not become a matter of concern until ancient printers discovered themselves with several different sizes of type on hand bearing no relation to each other. All types until this time apparently had been cut for specific printing jobs, with no relationship to other sizes already available.

Names Evolve to Represent Sizes

In the English-speaking world, no system existed with wide acceptance until near the turn of the twentieth century. Instead, printers found themselves saddled with a group of sizes having strange-sounding names such as Minion, Brevier, Bourgeois, Long Primer, English, Pica, Small Pica and the like. These names represented *sizes*, not faces, and even today, a reference to these names might be found in a dated printing textbook. Historians suggest these names, and the sizes they represented, evolved from first use of such types. Thus, the name *Brevier* was said "to derive its name from extensive use in printing Roman Catholic Breviaries or prayer books," and *Bourgeois* was said "to have been dedicated to the French master printers (les Bourgeois), and another reason was that it was first produced in the town of Bourges. *French Canon* was supposed to have been produced by some artist to suit the Church dignitaries in printing works relating to the Canons of the Church. The German name 'Missal' for that size gives force to this interpretation."[1]

The one term still found in popular usage is *Pica*. It too apparently had its origin with Church printing.

> Pica. The Rev. E. Morse Rowe, a great literary author and antiquarian, born in Kent in 1729, in his "Dissertation upon English Typographical Founders," says "The *Pie* was a table showing the course of the service in the Church in the times of darkness and was written in narrow columns of black and red. There were some Friars in England called *Friars de Pie,* so called for their party coloured raiment, black and white striped like the plumage of a magpie. Another definition is from *Pie,* an old Roman Catholic service book, so called from the manner of its printing, presenting an appearance like the colours of a magpie. An old placard of Caxton's preserved at Oxford reads thus, "If it please any man spirituelle or temporal to buy any *pyes,* two or three, let him come to Westminster and he shall have them good and chepe." The French and Germans call it "Cicero", so possibly the writings of that philosopher were printed in it. . . .[2]

Lack of System First Noted

Thus, the manner in which the printing trade got its various type sizes was far from being scientific. Even though it was very late in the nineteenth century before any sizing system came to be accepted, writers bewailed the lack of such a system almost from the beginning. In fact, the very first technical book on the art of printing, Joseph Moxon's *Mechanick Exercises,* printed in 1683, argued the subject. Therein he made note of ten popu-

---

[1]"Type Bodies," *The British Printer, Stationery and Fancy Trades Gazette,* 3:14 (March-April, 1890), 11.
[2]Ibid.

lar sizes of type in use in England and equated their sizes by listing the number of bodies of each fitting into one foot. Then he noted, "These are the bodies most used in England; but the *Dutch* have several other Bodies, which, because there is little and almost no perceivable difference from some of these mentioned, I think they are not worth naming."[3] Dutch types often were used in England at that time, so it can be concluded that variances in body sizes were of concern to printers.

There being no other way of demonstrating the relative sizes of types, several founders through the years resorted to printing tables showing the various bodies lined up together. The American typefounder, James Ronaldson of Philadelphia, included such a table in his 1822 specimen book "for comparing the relative proportions of the depth of line from Great Primer to Pearl."[4] In 1824, J. Johnson expressed his aggrevation by the following statement in his *Typographica,* published in England:

> Though all founders agree in the point of casting letters to certain Bodies, yet in the article of casting each body always to one and the same size, they differ; insomuch that not only founders of different places, but of the same residence, and even each in particular, often vary in height and depth. . . ."[5]

Johnson bemoaned the fact that even in the best-regulated offices, it was impossible to prevent sorts from

[3]Joseph Moxon, *Mechanick Exercises: Or the Doctrine of Handy-Works Applied to the Art of Printing,* Vol. II (London: Printed for Joseph Moxon at the West Side of Fleet Ditch at the Sign of Atlas, 1683), 13.

[4]*Specimen of Printing Types from the Letter Foundry of James Ronaldson, Successor to Binny & Ronaldson* (Philadelphia: James Ronaldson, 1822), last page of book.

[5]J. Johnson, *Typographica, or the Printers' Instructor,* Vol. II (London: Longman, Hurst, Rees, Orme, Brown & Green, 1824), 13.

TABLE for comparing the relative proportions in the depth of line from Great Primer to Pearl:

——:——

N° 1 Great Primer.
N° 2 English.
N° 3 Columbian.
N° 4 Pica.
N° 5 Small Pica.
N° 6 Long Primer.
N° 7 Bourgeois.
N° 8 Brevier.
N° 9 Minion.
N° 10 Nonpareil.
N° 11 Pearl.

N° 1	2	3	4	5	6	7	8	9	10	11
1	1	1	1	1	1	1	1	1	1	1
2	2	2	2	3	3	3	3	3	4	5
3	3	3	4	4	5	5	5	6	7	8
4	5	5	5	6	6	7	7	8	10	12
5	6	6	7	8	8	9	9	10	13	16
6	7	7	8	9	10	11	12	13	16	19
7	8	8	10	11	12	13	14	15	19	23
8	10	10	11	12	13	15	16	18	22	26
9	11	11	13	14	15	17	18	20	25	30
10	12	12	14	16	17	19	20	22	28	34
11	13	13	15	17	19	21	22	25	31	37
12	15	15	17	19	20	23	24	27	34	41
13	16	16	18	21	22	25	26	29	37	45
14	17	17	20	22	24	27	29	32	40	48
15	18	18	21	24	26	29	31	34	43	52
16	20	20	23	26	27	31	33	36	46	56
17	21	21	24	27	29	33	35	39	49	59
18	22	22	25	29	31	35	37	41	52	63
19	23	23	27	31	33	37	39	43	55	67
20	25	25	28	32	34	39	41	46	58	70
21	26	26	30	34	36	41	43	48	61	74
22	27	27	31	35	38	43	46	51	64	77
23	28	28	33	37	40	45	48	53	67	81
24	30	30	34	39	41	47	50	55	70	85
25	31	31	36	40	43	49	52	58	73	88
26	32	32	37	42	45	51	54	60	76	92

James Ronaldson's presentation of type sizes for visual comparison.

being mixed, made by different founders and varying in size only enough to ruin the printed piece wherein they were mixed.

As typefounding grew, the confusion over type sizes multiplied, both in England and the United States. The matter reached its worst proportions in the 1880's, when one writer complained, "It may be said without a violation of truth that practically there are no two foundries in the United States whose body types, either in depth or width, are cast by the same standard. This lack of uniformity has not only been a source of annoyance and loss to the majority of proprietors but too often a bone of contention between employer and employee."[6]

Early Suggestions for Systems

This is not to suggest that systems for type sizing had not been devised. On the contrary, several were suggested from time to time; some were even put into practice. In the English-speaking world, one of the earliest proposals came from James Fergusson of Scotland in 1824. He suggested Nonpareil as standard, fitting 12 to the inch, and that all other type sizes be even divisions of 14 Nonpareils. The scheme never got beyond the proposition stage.[7]

The Bower Brothers foundry, in 1841, published *Proposals for Establishing a Graduated Scale of Sizes for the Bodies of Printing Types, and Fixing their Height to Paper Based upon Pica as the Common Standard and Referable to the English Inch.* Therein it was suggested that the Pica equal

---

[6]"Standard Measurement," *Inland Printer*, 2:3 (December, 1884), 110.

[7]R. C. Elliott, "The Development of the 'Point' Unit of Type Measurement," *The Monotype Recorder*, 30:241 (1931), 15.

a sixth of an inch, and that each Pica contain 16 "points." Each type size would be a fixed number of points.[8] This system also received little note.

A decimal system was conceived and introduced in 1857 by the Shanks Patent Type Foundry in England, wherein the Pica would be 20 points, and would measure .1667 inch. The Nonpareil would be 10 points. The foundry used this system for several years.[9]

SHANKS' DECIMAL SYSTEM

Body	Pt.	Inch	Body	Pt.	Inch
Semi-Nonpareil	5	0.0417	Brevier	13	0.1083
Brilliant	6	0.0500	Bourgeois	14	0.1167
Diamond	7	0.0583	Long Primer	16	0.1333
Pearl	8	0.0667	Small Pica	18	0.1500
Ruby	9	0.0750	Pica	20	0.1667
Nonpareil	10	0.0833	English	22	0.1833
Minion	12	0.1000			

All these systems were arranged on arithmetic subdivisions. In 1822, in the United States, the Bruce typefoundry came up with a geometric system for sizing its type. The company adopted the system and continued to cast its type on this system even after the point system had been adopted by nearly all other founders.[10] With the Bruce system, each size of type was 12.2462+ per cent larger than the size immediately preceding it. The system was arranged so that it would double with

---

[8]*Proposals for Establishing a Graduated Scale of Sizes for the Bodies of Printing Types* . . . (3d ed.; Sheffield: Bower Brothers, 1841), 4.

[9]Lucien A. Legros and John C. Grant, *Typographical Printing Surfaces* (London: Logmans, Green, and Co., 1916), 67.

[10]"Uniformity in Type Bodies," *Inland Printer,* 8:1 (October, 1890), 71.

SIZES OF PRINTING TYPES.

The following *Standard* for the bodies of Type originated by GEORGE BRUCE, in the year 1822, has been found very satisfactory. It disturbs but trivially the sizes which are most used, while it fixes the body of every size in exact and correct proportion with the other sizes. This Standard is based on the system of Geomatrical Progression, doubling at every seventh size in any part of the series. Each size is, therefore, 12.2462+ per cent. larger than the size immediately above it, as shown in the following columns:

BODY.	Size in Decimals of a Linear Inch.	Body larger than that preceding it, in Decimals of a Linear Inch.	Ems and Decimals of an Em in a Linear Foot.	Ems and Decimals of an Em in a Square Foot.
DIAMOND	.0595+		201.587+	40,637.46+
PEARL	.0668+	.0072+	179.593+	32,253.97+
AGATE	.075	.0081+	160.	25,600.
NONPAREIL	.0841+	.0091+	142.543+	20,318.73+
MINION	.0994+	.0103+	126.992+	16,126.98+
BREVIER	.1060+	.0115+	113.137+	12,800.
BOURGEOIS	.1190+	.0129+	100.793+	10,159.36+
LONG-PRIMER	.1336+	.0145+	89.796+	8,063.49+
SMALL-PICA	.15	.0163+	80.	6,400.
PICA	.1683+	.0183+	71.271+	5,079.68+
ENGLISH	.1889+	.0206+	63.496+	4,031.74+
COLUMBIAN	.2121+	.0231+	56.568+	3,200.
GREAT-PRIMER	.2381+	.0259+	50.396+	2,539.84+
PARAGON	.2672+	.0291+	44.898+	2,015.87+
DOUBLE SMALL-PICA	.3	.0327+	40.	1,600.
DOUBLE PICA	.3367+	.0367+	35.635+	1,269.92+
DOUBLE ENGLISH	.3779+	.0412+	31.748+	1,007.93+
DOUBLE COLUMBIAN	.4242+	.0462+	28.284+	800.
DOUBLE GREAT-PRIMER	.4762+	.0519+	25.198+	634.96+
DOUBLE PARAGON	.5345+	.0583+	22.449+	503.96+
MERIDIAN	.6	.0654+	20.	400.
CANON	.6734+	.0734+	17.817+	317.48+

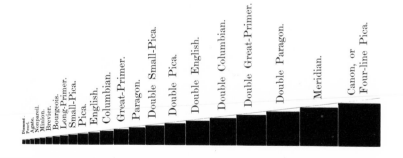

George Bruce's geometric system of type sizes.

every seventh size.[11] Although ingenious, the system resulted in a most cumbersome set of dimensions and was not adopted by other founders.

The Fournier System

What eventually proved to be the system adopted in the English-speaking world antedates all systems or proposals mentioned thus far, and came not from England or the United States, but from France. An attempt to remedy the state of confusion over type sizing was made by official decree in Paris in 1723.[12] The regulation theoretically established type height, but was far from precise in establishing type sizes. It specified the relationships between various sizes, so that two lines of one size would equal one of another, but failed to specify the exact size of the smaller units. Thus, a typefounder could make his type any size and still conform as long as his faces were doubles of each other.

> In the absence of better knowledge on this subject, a master printer gave for a standard, with all their imperfections, such types as he found in his own printing office. The regulation based on this standard, not being founded on any proper basis, has not been complied with. This is the reason why the bodies of types have never had fixed and accurate dimensions, and why the irregularity is just as great now as it was before the regulation. . . .[13]

These were the words of Pierre Simon Fournier, who decided in 1737 that he would give reality to the regula-

---

[11]*Specimens of Printing Types Made at Bruce's New York Type Foundry* (New York: George Bruce's Son & Co., 1882), preface.

[12]Walter Tracy, "The Point," *The Penrose Annual*, 55 (1961), 63.

[13]Theodore L. DeVinne, *The Practice of Typography: A Treatise on the Process of Type-Making, the Point System, The Names, Sizes, Styles and Prices of Plain Printing Types* (2d ed.; New York: The Century Press, 1902, 134.

tion of 1723 by instituting what he called a system of "typographic points." The system was described in the form of a printed table, included in his specimen book *Modeles des Caracteres* in 1742, and referred to in the preface of that work. More elaborate description followed in the first volume of his famous *Manuel Typographique* of 1764,[14] from which the quotation above was derived.

Fournier's system was carefully worked out so that each type size was an exact number of points. Universal acceptance of today's point system makes detailed discussion unnecessary, for they are nearly the same. The pre-metric French inch was to contain six "Ciceros" (French equivalent of Pica) or 12 "Nompareilles," and each Nompareille was given the definite value of six points. Thus, the inch would contain 72 points. With each size having a precise point body, it is evident that all sizes would work with each other; this fact was explained in great detail in Fournier's "Tables des Proportions," which illustrated what today is taken for granted (e. g. two lines of Parisienne equal one line of Petit-Romain —two lines of 5 point equal one of 10 point).

Fournier's system by no means achieved instant success, for in his *Manuel Typographique* of 1764, he called it "new and unknown."[15] Nevertheless, by the time of his death, Fournier's system generally had been adopted as a standard by French typefounders.

The downfall of his system was that it did not conform precisely to the official French measure, the pre-metric "Royal Foot." His rough diagram accompanying

---

[14]Tracy, op. cit., 64.   [15]DeVinne, op. cit., 133.

the "Tables des Proportions" suggested the system was based on two inches of official measure, yet nowhere in his *Manuel* did he refer to "any standard measure for verification of the accuracy of his scale or prototype."[16]

The Didot System

Another famous typefounder in France, Francois Ambroise Didot, suggested Fournier's system should be based definitely upon the legal foot measure of France. With the help of his son, Firmin, the first types cast on this system were issued in 1783 or 1784.[17] The system enlarged the point somewhat, making the old Fournier Cicero equal to about 11 Didot points. Instead of relying on names, Didot gave each size a number, such as *"corps* (body) *6."* For a while, the then-outdated term Cicero was related to what, on the Didot scale, was the 11-point size; this measure was indivisible and, therefore, quite cumbersome. Cicero had been the traditional unit of general measure, like the Pica in England and the United States, so printers soon found it advantageous to relate Cicero to the larger 12-point Didot size.[18]

The Didot system had its opponents too. "But the great reputation of the Didot family . . . overcame opposition to the new point system, and it rapidly gained favor."[19] It remains in use on much of the Continent today, even though it now suffers as did the Fournier system; it is no longer related to any legal basis of meas-

---

[16]Ibid., 141.

[17]Felix Smalian, "Who Discovered and Perfected the French Typographical Point?" *Inland Printer,* 70:5 (February, 1923), 672.

[18]Elliott, op. cit., 14.

[19]Tracy, loc. cit.

ure. The metric system was given legal status in France in 1801 and the inch—on which the Didot system is based—was abandoned.

While the French were working first with the Fournier system and later with the Didot system, counterparts in both Britain and the United States struggled with a series of proposals which brought little action. And as the typefounding industry in these two countries grew, the lack of a standard seemed to further complicate itself. Indeed, as one founder stated in 1870, "The problem of making the whole series of bodies so that they will work with each other is one which cannot well be satisfactorily solved."[20]

It is curious to note that this comment was made by a man whose typefounding firm would successfully introduce the system which *did* "satisfactorily solve" the problem—and only seven years after the comment was made.

---

[20]"Gossip with Correspondents and Readers," *The Chicago Specimen,* 4:4 (October, 1870), 3-4.

Chapter Two

Cry for Reform

TYPE FOUNDERS THEMSELVES were not bothered by the irregularity of type bodies during most of the nineteenth century. Their chief concern was that of issuing new and novel type designs, and with keeping up on orders for new fonts and sorts cast to the standards they had in daily use—regardless of how irregular or haphazard those standards might have been. Generally, the founders did not use type. If they were to do any composition for promotional work, a specimen book or the like, chances were very slim that they would have the products of other foundries in their composing rooms to cause confusion.

But there was plenty of confusion in the various printing offices, where, for various reasons, the products of several typefounders often were mixed. Therefore, the call for reform—for standardization—came from outside the typefounding fraternity. It came from country printers and trade publication editors who sensed the need and tried to do something about it.

A modern-day student of printing cannot begin to comprehend the problem until he realizes that 30 or more type foundries operated independently of each other in the United States alone during the period between 1850 and 1885. At this time, all type was hand type. The Linotype, Monotype, and other devices for mechanizing composition still were in the future. Such a

simple modern-day convenience as a calibrated composing stick was impossible, for there was no standard which
the calibrations could represent. The "comp" had to set
his stick by assembling a row of "ems" to the desired
length, always with the risk of grabbing a "wrong font"
em and throwing off his measure.

Campaign Waged for a Standard

. . .While the disadvantages of the present system, each
type founder being a law unto himself, have been exper-
ienced by nine printers out of ten, even in our larger cities, it
is the *country printer* who feels them most keenly, because he is
most frequently victimized. A hurried job of importance is
received; sorts, most likely cap, figures, or leaders, are lacking
to complete the job. If a printer's supply depot is in town, and
the needed sorts are in stock, which is very seldom the case,
they are gladly accepted and no questions asked (we suppose
on the principle that beggars should not be choosers) though
the chances are the purchaser will find to his disgust that they
do not justify with the material on hand.[1]

This was the gist of a strong editorial in the *Inland
Printer,* a respected and active trade publication during
that era. The argument was fairly representative of
complaints being voiced by printers across the country.
One job printer wrote the magazine with this comment
regarding the profusion of sizes in his shop:

In the little country office in which I bear the empty title of
foreman, there are four sizes of Great Primer, two of Small
Pica, two of Long Primer, two of Brevier, and two of Nonpareil. 'From different foundries,' says some typefounder.
Yes and no, I answer. In Brevier body-type, all from one
foundry (name no matter) the em quads are too small, making it almost impossible to lift a moderate handful. In Non-

---

[1]"Standard Measurement," *Inland Printer,* 2:3 (December, 1884), 110.

An advertisement for perhaps one of the very first composing sticks "on the point system" was this stick, produced by the Golding Company. In reviewing the invention in 1886, the Inland Printer *noted "it is only adjustable to Picas and Nonpareils of the standard adopted by the majority of the foundries for the new American system. . . . The measures are stamped on the stick and no quads are needed in setting it."*

pareil, from the same foundry, bought at different times, but carefully ordered from same numbers, and by the additional precaution of sending sample letters, there are two thicknesses of periods and commas, and a variation in the body that makes a beautiful mess when a table is set using the old figures and the new letters.[2]

The cry for standardization had different meaning for each person bothered by the lack of any "standard." The printer quoted above was calling for all founders to cast their types on the same size bodies. At the same time, he was calling for the fixing of "sets" so that sorts ordered at different times from the same founder would match up. Matters of alignment, fixed set for all different faces, standard set widths for figures and spaces, and even standardized font schemes—all were grouped under a listing of grievances against typefounders, collectively and individually.

Typefounders Reply

In reacting to complaints voiced in the *Inland Printer* and other trade journals of that period, typefounders stated they had not ignored the question of standardization. Rather, the matter had received long and careful attention throughout the United States. "And the more its feasibility has been investigated, the more formidable have the difficulties attendant on its adoption appeared. . . . "[3]

Expenses for re-tooling to cast new bodies, disposition of stock currently on hand, and precisely *whose* standard would be used—all were factors used to build the typefounders' argument. One founder estimated

[2]"A Word to Type-founders," *Inland Printer*, 2:6 (April, 1885), 305.
[3]"Standard Measurement," *Inland Printer*, 2:5 (February, 1885), 211.

re-tooling alone would cost from $75,000 to $100,000, and that some founders had as much as 10 million pounds of material, representing their current type bodies, scattered over the length and breadth of the country.[4]

The same founder suggested that most of the problem had been created by printers buying material from distant foundries. "I believe . . . the annoyance . . . would be removed if western printers would patronize western typefounders, and eastern printers order from eastern founders. . . ."[5]

Which standard would be adopted was, perhaps, the paramount concern of the typefounders. If the standard of a given foundry were adopted, what then? "Would it not give a virtual monopoly of the trade, for the time being at least, to the one firm at the expense of all others? Is it at all likely that the successful firm would be willing to share even a part of its profits with its less fortunate competitors?"[6] The answer was no, and the agreement, therefore, was that no standard could be adopted.

Responding to these objections the *Inland Printer* said, "We insist the end would justify the means, and that these and similar objections would be overshadowed by the general and permanent advantages ultimately conferred on the craft at large."[7]

Editorial crossfire continued, but independently, various typefounders made attempts at establishing some sort of standard. The Bruce Type Foundry of New

---

[4]Ibid.   [5]Ibid.

[6]Ibid.

[7]"Standard Measurement," *Inland Printer*, 2:3 (December, 1884), 110.

York continued its claim to the only logical system, adding that it had been instituted by George Bruce himself in 1822.[8] The Cleveland Type Foundry and the MacKellar, Smiths and Jordan foundry of Philadelphia initiated a system whereby the Pica was subdivided into eight equal units.[9] Since type was to be sized by half-unit steps, this system was precisely the same as that proposed by England's Bower Brothers foundry—a 16-point Pica—in 1841. And independently of all others, the Marder, Luse and Company foundry of Chicago had instituted a system subdividing the Pica into 12 equal units. The move had been made in secrecy and the first types on the system were made in 1877.

Today it is obvious that the system introduced by Marder, Luse and Company was the one which finally succeeded. The story of how it was devised and how it gradually was accepted by the American and British typefounding industry is a most interesting chapter in the history of printing.

---

[8]"Proportions of Type," *The Printers Miscellany* (published by George Bruce & Co.) undated.

[9]N. J. Werner, Postscript to "Who Discovered and Perfected the French Typographical Point System?" by Felix Smalian, *Inland Printer,* 70:5 (February, 1923), 672.

Chapter Three

Marder, Luse & Co. Adopts System

TYPEFOUNDING had proliferated at an extremely rapid rate during the mid-nineteenth century, and competition at times was rigorous. Thus, rather than seeking to establish a "standard" for the industry, Marder, Luse and Company sought a competitive advantage when the firm first introduced the idea of a system for sizing type bodies.

Searching back to find the origin of ML&Co. gives some understanding of how typefounding spread to the West during the nineteenth century. First established as a Chicago branch for the New York-based White typefoundry, ML&Co., as an independent enterprise, ended up with its own branches. Its first branch was established at San Francisco in 1874, and by the time the firm was absorbed into the newly created American Type Founders conglomerate in 1892, ML&Co. had other branches in Omaha, Minneapolis, St. Paul and Kansas City,[1] as well as independent distributors in other cities.

History of the Foundry

Typefounding was still a mysterious art when Elihu White joined William Wing of Hartford, Connecticut, in 1804 to enter into the typefounding business. Repeated

---

[1]"Special Announcement, American Typefounders' Company," *Inland Printer,* 10:5 (February, 1893), 399.

failure at devising their own apparatus finally forced them to send a representative to study the trade at the Binny and Ronaldson foundry in Philadelphia, the nation's first successful foundry.[2] After doing a limited business in Hartford, White separated from Wing, moving his foundry to New York in 1810. Success brought the need for him to establish branch foundries in Buffalo and Cincinnati. When he died in 1836, the business was continued by his son, John T. White. Later, John was succeeded by Norman White, and when Norman's son joined the firm, it was renamed Charles T. White and Company.[3] In 1855, Charles T. White and Company opened a branch foundry in Chicago, calling it the Chicago Type Foundry.

When Charles T. White retired from the business, he sold his interest to his employees, A. D. Farmer, Andrew Little and John Bentley.[4] Farmer, Little and Company sold its Chicago branch in 1863 and the Chicago operation became known as D. Schofield & Company; a year later the firm became known as Schofield, Marder & Company, with John Marder becoming a partner.[5] Partnership changes continued until 1869, when A. P. Luse joined the firm. Luse had operated a successful printing establishment in Davenport, Iowa, and at one time employed Marder at Davenport.[6] In that year, the firm's name became fixed as Marder, Luse and

---

[2]Theodore L. DeVinne, *The Practice of Typography. A Treatise on the Process of Type-Making* . . . (2d ed.; New York: The Century Press, 1902), 102.

[3]Ibid.   [4]Ibid.

[5]Ibid.

[6]James Eckman, "The Chicago Type Foundry of Marder, Luse and Company, 1863-1892," *Printing and Graphic Arts,* 7:3 (September, 1959), 69-70.

This cover of Marder, Luse and Company's house organ, The Chicago Specimen, *illustrates both the foundry's history and the varied items on hand for sale. Its small beginning was in 1855; the business had enlarged its quarters by 1865; it was left in complete ruin by the fire of 1871; then a new and larger facility was completed by 1876. Hawks' iron bracketed stand is illustrated by the second-floor window on the left side of the page.*

A. P. Luse as depicted in the Inland Printer *in 1891.*

John Marder–from Paper & Press, *January 1888.*

Company,[7] even though Schofield maintained a minor interest in the firm until 1880.[8]

When established as a branch of the White firm, the Chicago operation was an outlet rather than a manufacturing firm. Rapid growth of the West in population and wealth and the consequent increase in demand for printers' supplies enabled the branch to give attention to the production of type. Typecasting facilities were added gradually, until by the time of the great Chicago fire of 1871, Marder, Luse and Company was making the greater portion of the materials it sold.[9] Production was completely halted by the fire, however. All the foundry's molds, matrices and machinery were destroyed.[10]

Rebuilding After the Chicago Fire

The typefoundry was rebuilt on a much larger scale following the fire, and an entire new beginning was made.[11] Carl Muller joined the firm as a partner[12] and became responsible for all the company's tooling —making the molds, matrices, maintaining typecasting machinery, etc. With this new beginning, ML&Co. made two decisions which, in a few years, would figure significantly in the introduction of the point system.

First was the decision to make new molds which would size Pica type exactly the same as that of the MacKellar, Smiths and Jordan foundry of

[7]DeVinne, op. cit.

[8]A. P. Luse, personal letter to N. C. Hawks, July 2, 1880.

[9]"Justification of Type Bodies," *The Chicago Specimen*, 10:1 (January, 1876), 2.

[10]"Marder, Luse and Company," *Paper and Press*, 6:1 (January, 1888), 22.

[11]Ibid.

[12]DeVinne, op. cit., 104.

Philadelphia,[13] successor to the aforementioned Binny and Ronaldson and perhaps the largest foundry in operation at the time. Border and job fonts from MS&J were in general use throughout the country, and by adopting that Pica, Marder, Luse and Company created for itself the opportunity of matching these fonts with many of its own.[14]

Although no system for sizing type existed among the typefounders of that day, there was a rule which, although not infallible, was *sometimes* adhered to: the rule related certain sizes to others as doubles of each other. This procedure established that:

One line of Minion	equals two lines of Brilliant
One line of Brevier	equals two lines of Minikin
One line of Bourgeois	equals two lines of Diamond
One line of Long Primer	equals two lines of Pearl
One line of Small Pica	equals two lines of Agate (or Ruby)
One line of Pica	equals two lines of Nonpareil
One line of English	equals two lines of Minion
One line of Columbian	equals two lines of Brevier
One line of Great Primer	equals two lines of Bourgeois
One line of Paragon	equals two lines of Long Primer[15]

Some Sizes Are Standardized

The proportions mentioned above did vary, however, and apparently did not hold true for the types of Marder, Luse and Company before the fire in 1871. Since all molds had to be re-made after the fire, the firm resolved to eliminate this discrepancy in type to be made

---

[13]John Marder, "Touching-Up the Type Founders," *The British & Colonial Printer & Stationer*, 31:3 (January 19, 1893), 2.

[14]Henry L. Bullen, "Nelson C. Hawks' 'Invention' of the American Point System," *Inland Printer*, 46:11 (August, 1929), 65.

[15]H. G. Bishop, "The Practical Printer," *Inland Printer*, 5:4 (January, 1888), 247.

in the new foundry. A new arrangement enabled ML&Co. to offer the printer four-step relationships, each size exactly doubling the one directly preceeding it laterally in the following scale:

Excelsior	Brevier	Columbian	Double Columbian
Diamond	Bourgeois	Great Primer	Double Great Primer
Pearl	Long Primer	Paragon	Double Paragon
Agate	Small Pica	Double Small Pica	Canon
Nonpareil	Pica	Double Pica	Four-Line Pica
Minion	English	Double English[16]	

It was only incidental, however, that relationships existed between the sizes as listed in vertical order. As the firm explained, "in *some* [italics added] of the bodies a two-line letter of one can be used with lines of two other sizes—as, for example, our Two-line Minion justifies with one of Brevier and one of Nonpareil."[17] Six independent sizes existed, then, on which all other sizes were multiples.

The firm had made a positive step toward simplifying the confusion over type sizes. However, this gives evidence of the fact that ML&Co. did not initiate the idea of the point system at this time, although later on, 1872 frequently was alluded to by the company as being the date of origin.

Nelson C. Hawks Joins Firm

As mentioned, ML&Co. sold many items, especially equipment related to the printing trade such as printshop furniture, presses, typecases and tools. One such item was a patented "Iron Bracket Composing Stand" which was obtained from Nelson C. Hawks, the

[16]"Justification of Type Bodies," op. cit.
[17]Ibid.

inventor, a partner in the Hawks and Burdick printing firm of Milwaukee. The stands, which held only one case at a time, claimed the advantage of "there being no cases below to rub . . . the shins."[18] The stands apparently were a desirable item, for they were reordered several times from Hawks by ML&Co.[19]

Perhaps these business dealings acquainted John Marder with Nelson C. Hawks. In 1874, Marder induced Hawks to sell his interest in the Milwaukee firm and go to San Francisco to establish an agency for Marder, Luse and Company in that city, and become a partner in the ML&Co. firm.[20]

In establishing an agency on the West Coast, ML&Co. was making a major effort to corner the growing West Coast trade in printing supplies. Printshops in the West which already had been established were supplied by other manufacturers, especially eastern founders.[21] Therefore, to be an effective supply house, Hawks' outlet had to maintain a supply of type from several manufacturers other than ML&Co. At this point in history, such was not an easy undertaking, for it was unusual to find types from different manufacturers which matched each other in size. Thus, Hawks had to stock, in addition to type, separate fonts of spacing, quads, borders, leads and so on, all from different manufacturers and varying in size only enough to pre-

[18]"Patents of Interest," *Inland Printer,* 3:10 (July, 1886), 626.

[19]A journal maintained by Hawks recording sales of the composing stand reveals several sales to ML&Co.

[20]William E. Loy, "Typefounders and Typefounding in America, No. XXVII—Nelson Crocker Hawks," *Inland Printer,* 23:2 (November, 1902), 249.

[21]Nelson C. Hawks, "How the Point System Was Started," *Printing Art,* 36:5 (January, 1921), 389.

vent mixing.[22] Spacing items, especially, differed so little that they caused much confusion at the San Francisco agency, bringing Hawks to ponder seriously the need for more uniformity in type bodies.

Idea for System Developed

Hawks explains that he spent many hours measuring different samples of types spread on his desk.

> Finding our own Pica to be one-sixth of an inch [see Chapter 6], the idea of adopting the mechanic's rule as a basis for measurement occurred to me. Then came the division of the Pica into parts. Nonpareil being one-half the size of Pica, the unit of measurement would have to be determined from the number of sizes above Nonpareil. These are Minion, Brevier, Bourgeois, Long Primer, Small Pica and Pica—six. Therefore, Nonpareil would be the other six, and Pica would be twelve points.[23]

With this simple and logical explanation, Hawks gave his reason for dividing the Pica into twelve units. Being convinced of the workability of his idea, Hawks awaited opportunity to discuss the matter with his partners in Chicago. Such an opportunity came in 1877 when John Marder visited California to "get Hawks away from business."

"Your recent letters convinced both Mr. Luse and myself that you were overworked and needed a change," Hawks quotes Marder as saying.[24] During a pleasure trip by rail to Santa Cruz, Hawks presented his idea of uniform type bodies, over Marder's strong objection.

Having been a practical printer, and having studied the matter in great detail, Hawks was able to explain the

---

[22] Ibid.   [23] Ibid.
[24] Ibid.

merits of the idea to Marder. Hawks quotes Marder as finally commenting, "Why these bodies work into each other all the way through!"[25] This was something which never had been possible under existing systems.

Nelson Hawks succeeded in his first effort at promoting his system, as noted modestly in his personal diary under the year 1877. Discussing Marder's visit: "During his stay we agreed to bring out the new system of type bodies."[26]

System Pursued in Secrecy

Hawks maintains that he refused to allow Marder to patent the system on the basis that it should be available to all typefounders as "a free gift for the benefit of the craft."[27] There is evidence that later on, Marder may have attempted to patent the idea,[28] but for the time being, he swore Hawks to secrecy so that Marder, Luse and Company would be able to get its new system into molds, and type into production before competitors could take note of the move. Soon after his return to Chicago in May, Marder wrote Hawks:

> Keep the thing quiet except I would say to customers how it can be done—not a soul except Muller knows our plan here and you must keep quiet on it. I am afraid Mr. L. will oppose it. You know he is very timid to take hold of a new thing but

---

[25]Ibid.

[26]Nelson Hawks kept a personal "Journal." Although entries were not made regularly, the entry quoted is under the year 1877.

[27]Charles A. Murdock, "History of Printing in San Francisco," *The Pacific Printer & Publisher,* 33:4 (April, 1925), 279.

[28]Ibid. Also, in a personal letter to Hawks dated May 31, 1879, A. P. Luse makes the statement, "Mr. Marder has the patent business in hand and will get the patent on new bodies if it is to be had." No patent on the bodies was granted. This, however, may be a reference to the trademark which was received for the title, "American System of Interchangeable Type Bodies."

Muller is with us all over. He is working like a trooper and studying the thing up so as to carry the thing in practice without a blunder.[29]

Apparently A. P. Luse did agree to the plan, or else he was forced by the other partners (Marder, Muller and Hawks) to accept it. Still, it was on Muller's shoulders that the weight of the new system fell most heavily. After his visit to California, Marder observed that "Muller is very busy getting his new molds started. The new letter must line on the bottom so we find we must put the smallest size on 'Columbian' body. They will run then 16, 18, 22, 28 and 36 lines according to the new standard."[30]

He was referring to a new typeface, Parallel Shaded, which was announced simultaneously in the summer of 1877 in *The Chicago Specimen* of ML&Co., and *The Pacific Specimen*, published in San Francisco by Hawks for ML&Co.

To get the new design into type, Muller had managed to create both new matrices and, in all probability, three new molds. This was accomplished in the few months between Marder's return from San Francisco in May and publication of the journals later in the summer. In the new system, ML&Co. saw a competitive advantage, and worked quickly to exploit that advantage.

---

[29]John Marder, undated letter to N. C. Hawks.
[30]John Marder, personal letter to N. C. Hawks, March 8, 1878.

Chapter Four

Other Founders Adopt Idea

THE INTRODUCTION of the point system by Marder, Luse and Company was not something completed overnight. Perhaps their greatest fear was that the firm would be unable to get the entire system into production before being "discovered" by another founder and out-maneuvered.

Thus, the issuance of Parallel Shaded in 1877 was made with the mere statement that the company now had the "new feature of making the sizes to 'line' at the bottom of the letter and to justify exactly with each other by sixths-of-Pica."[1] Other early faces introduced on the point system were "Norman Condensed," issued in the fourth quarter, 1877, and "Pearl Roman" in the fourth quarter, 1878. None was introduced with much fanfare concerning the point system.

Hawks Breaks Secrecy

Nelson Hawks was much less inclined to keep the new system secret. He went so far as to issue a circular on the new system in 1878[2] which brought this response from A. P. Luse at the home foundry in Chicago:

---

[1]"Late Specimens," *The Chicago Specimen,* 11:3 (Third Quarter, 1877), 3.

[2]Hawks says in an account of the introduction of the point system appearing in *The Printing Art* magazine, 36:5 (January, 1921), that his announcement was made first in *The Pacific Specimen.* Close scrutiny of all issues of this publication during this time period reveals no such mention. The circular referred to here apparently was issued separately by Hawks. See Appendix, page 89.

Mr. Marder thinks you have put out your circular too soon and thinks you had better suppress it until we are more prepared. He and Mr. Muller think that some of the other foundries will get hold of it and beat us or make some check movement. . . ."[3]

Still, Hawks vigorously promoted the system on the West Coast. A sample of his enthusiasm is shown by this note in *The Pacific Specimen,* first quarter, 1879.

Years hence, and long after the members of this present firm are laid to rest, the printing craft will more fully understand and appreciate that which we are now doing for them, in emancipating all irregularities of type composition and justification, by means of our new and perfect system of bodies. To deliberately overthrow the work of years, on which a large business has been built, and a snug fortune spent, and begin all over again, is a thing that requires some courage; and as we have taken the great work in hand, both here and in Chicago, without a dime's assistance from those it directly benefits, it requires money also, as well as courage, and a good deal of it.[4]

A. P. Luse's reaction to this enthusiasm: "You want to be very careful about the bodies, or you will find yourself in an awful sea of trouble."[5] So Hawks took another route by printing letters from customers, such as the following. After saying the *San Mateo* (Calif.) *Journal* had been outfitted by the Pacific Type Foundry, Hawks quoted the newspaper as saying:

They [ML&Co.] are laboring hard to bring typemaking down to a perfect science, so that all types shall be fractional proportionate parts of all other types, with a true ratio running between. Nothing but the jealousy of other foundries will prevent the idea from prevailing through all.[6]

---

[3]A. P. Luse, personal letter to N. C. Hawks, August 24, 1878.
[4]"New Type Bodies," *The Pacific Specimen,* 4-1 (First Quarter, 1879), 2.
[5]A. P. Luse, personal letter to N. C. Hawks, February 24, 1879.
[6]"The Journal's Outfit," *San Mateo County* (Calif.) *Journal,* Nov. 27, 1879.

Later on, personal conflicts separated Hawks from the Marder-Luse partnership and subsequently, Marder accepted personal responsibility for creating and introducing the system. Therefore, it is significant to note here that articles from the West Coast during this period frequently linked Hawks' name with the innovation. The following is an example:

> In the way of inventions to printers, Mr. Hawks is the greatest philanthropist of the present decade. The new and uniform system of type bodies proposed by himself and carried to completion by his company, in Chicago, Marder, Luse & Company, is as great a perfection of type material as the Hoe press is better than the press used by John Gutenberg.[7]

In Chicago, the approach to the new system was less vocal, but nevertheless, aggressive. In 1879 Marder attempted to obtain a trademark for the system's name: "The American System of Interchangeable Type Bodies."[8]

Parallel Shaded and other early point system faces were cast only in larger sizes. As late as October, 1879, the complete range of sizes still was not ready, although the firm was anxious to achieve that goal, as Luse reported to Hawks.

> We are just acheing [sic.] to get out our Romans so we can fill an entire outfit on new bodies. It has worked a little awkward for the two years past, and it will take two years more before we can get out of trouble but when we do we will be compelled to double our machine capacity to get out our orders. 'Now don't you forget it.'[9]

---

[7]This clipping, dated August 28, 1880, is from a newspaper identified only as *The Plaindealer,* and is among several kept in a scrapbook by Hawks, now preserved in the Kemble Collections at the California Historical Society.

[8]A. P. Luse, personal letter to N. C. Hawks, May 31, 1879.

[9]Ibid., October 3, 1879.

First Official Announcement

Full details of the new system were first announced through *The Chicago Specimen,* third quarter, 1879. Siding with printers of that day by claiming "systems" of *other* founders drove job printers "to the verge of desperation," ML&Co. hailed the American System of Interchangeable Type Bodies as a "practical revolution."

> To compensate themselves, or to secure in the dim future an adequate return for their outlay and trouble, the inventors of the system, and the proprietors of the trade marks, have taken steps to secure their right to the undisturbed enjoyment of the American System of Interchangeable Type Bodies. This has been done through no fear of attempts to pirate the system throughout, as that would be an experiment too costly for many of this class of competitors to undertake; but they wish to be in a position to protect their customers from imposition by those who might try the less costly device of copying some of the names by which the new sizes are to be known, or adopting the name of the system itself.[10]

John Marder carried copies of the *Specimen* to the New York meeting of the Type Founders' Association that fall, and created "quite an excitement." Marder reported, "MacKellar, Smiths and Jordan have been working on the same thing for two years. Even Bruce (of the New York foundry) was worked up about it and wanted a copy. . . ."[11]   The firm's candle was no longer hidden under the bushel. At last Marder, Luse and Company would discover whether job printers would be impressed enough with the system to change the type bodies in their own shops.

---

[10]Extracted from a full-page ad describing the American System of Interchangeable Type Bodies. *Chicago Specimen,* 13:3&4 (Third Quarter, 1879), 2.

[11]A. P. Luse, personal letter to N. C. Hawks, November 5, 1879.

THE AMERICAN SYSTEM OF INTERCHANGEABLE TYPE BODIES.

EVERY Job Printer of considerable experience knows how annoying it is, when endeavoring to combine different sizes of type in the same line, to find that his material will not justify. It often wants the thickness of a sheet of cardboard, or a slip of paper, to render the packing of the two in the same line practicable. The trimming of cardboard or paper consumes time. When the line is set in this manner and packed in the form, it may be discovered that the letters are so cut on the respective bodies of the two sizes, that when printed, the alignment is imperfect. But even when the result secured this way goes, when it comes to distributing the form in which the line has stood for some time, the make-shift will be found not to have finished its mission as a time-killer. The types often cling to such a strip with exasperating tenacity. Type set in this manner being carefully distributed, will generally be found to have adhering to them small lumps of hard, dry paper pulp, which must be scraped off before the same pieces can be used again.

When the differences in body of the types, to be employed in the same line, is too great to be rectified by paper or cardboard, it then becomes necessary to resort to *leads*. Here the obstacle to the way of rapid and artistic work is that the type bodies and leads do not bear any such relation to each other as to admit of their being used in every instance just where they are most needed. The consequence is that the design must be abandoned, or the defects of material supplied by other contrivances.

When the work requires the employment of larger initial letters in alignment with two or more of smaller body, the Job Printer is driven to the verge of desperation by the discovery that he has no two small bodies which exactly equal the larger. To be sure, if he happens to find what he requires in any of the standard two-line bodies, his difficulties are measurably reduced. But the knowledge that he must conform his design to the arbitrary caprices of the type founder, is a constant clog on his fancy. So few of the sizes are exact factors of other sizes that he must curb a desire for tasteful display within the narrow limits prescribed by necessity.

Now the impracticability of using cards and slips of paper to eke out imperfect justification, lies in the fact that such things were never designed for such uses. They are neither graduated in thickness, nor composed of proper material to meet such emergencies satisfactorily. The difficulty with the lead is that it is graded in size according to the Pica body. There are other sizes not susceptible of combination with Pica, and consequently not with Pica leads.

It is unnecessary to enumerate them, as they are familiar to every printer of twelve months' experience.

The CHICAGO TYPE FOUNDRY has for years been working up a system of type bodies, embracing leads and rules, by which they shall become interchangeable throughout. In doing this the proprietors have been forced to act independently, other founders, to whom this matter has been presented to secure their co-operation, have seen proper to ignore its importance. MARDER, LUSE & CO. have shouldered the entire responsibility and expense of this reform, involving a decided change in some of the bodies heretofore in use, and the construction of implements and machinery for the manufacture of new bodies.

No.	Name	No.	Name
1	American	24	Double Pica
1½	German		
2	Saxon	28	Double English
2½	Norse		
3	Brilliant		
3½	Ruby	32	Dbl. Columbian
4	Excelsior		
4½	Diamond	36	Dbl. Grt. Primer
5	Pearl		
5½	Agate		
6	Nonpareil	40	Dbl. Paragon
7	Minion		
8	Brevier		
9	Bourgeois	44	Canon
10	Long Primer		
11	Small Pica	48	Four-Line Pica
12	Pica		
14	English		
16	Columbian	60	Five-Line Pica
18	Great Primer		
20	Paragon	72	Six-Line Pica
22	Dbl. Small Pica		

The above illustrations show the sizes of the different bodies, and their proportions to each other by twelfths of Pica, the present Pica being the standard.

Each size is a factor. Three Nonpareils (6) are a Great Primer (18); three Breviers (8) are a Double Pica (24); a Nonpareil (6) and a Brevier (8) are an English (14) or Two-line Minion; a Pica (12) and an Excelsior (4)—two six-to-Pica Leads—are a Columbian (16); a Double English (28) and a Brevier (8) are a Double Great Primer (36); so with all of the other sizes, making the combination of two or more sizes of Type in a word, or line, the simplest thing imaginable in composition. That odd body, Bourgeois (9), is now a respectable size, being a Nonpareil (6) and one-half exactly. •

Look over the figures and test the simplicity of the new system of Type bodies.

By reason of the destruction of their moulds and matrices in the fire of '71, a new start was rendered necessary, thus enabling them to make this important change with less trouble and expense than it would incur upon other founders, and also decrease the liability of mixing the old with the new bodies.

The importance of this change as an item of expense to them may be approximately estimated by any one, even slightly acquainted with the practical details of type making. The advantages of the new system to the Job Printer will be best appreciated by himself.

To compensate themselves, or to secure in the dim future an adequate return for their outlay and trouble, the inventors of the system, and the proprietors of the trade marks, have taken steps to secure their right to the undisturbed enjoyment of the *American System of Interchangeable Type Bodies*. This has been done through no fear of attempts to pirate the system throughout, as that would be an experiment too costly for many of this class of competitors to undertake; but they wish to be in a position to protect their customers from imposition by those who might try the less costly device of copying some of the names by which the new sizes are to be known, or adopting the name of the system itself.

This system, briefly explained, consists in adopting as the unit of measurement for all type bodies, the *American*, which is exactly one-twelfth of Pica. This is the smallest and is applied only to leads and rules. All the other bodies bear exact relations to this as indicated by numbers. From *American* to *Nonpareil*, which is numbered 6, they increase progressively by one-half the body of the first. Beyond this, to *Pica*, by an increase of the size of American. There are no *bastard* or irregular sizes. Applying this explanation to the subjoined table, the beauty and utility of the new system will be apparent at a glance.

Printers will be able to appropriate the advantages of this change with much greater facility, and much less expense than it has been made by the type founders, and the benefits will prove incalculable to those who adopt it.

The reason why this radical change is so difficult and expensive is that it could not be successfully carried out upon the patch-work principle. Had the founders been content to accomplish the work by introducing one slight change after another, the result would have been to introduce confusion wherever their new bodies were mixed with the old. It required a practical revolution in the entire system. This has at length been accomplished, and we feel proud of the fact that the institution of a reform of such magnitude should have been reserved to a Chicago foundry, and our own *Chicago Type Foundry* at that.

We have now in course of preparation a Specimen Book containing various styles of Roman and Job Type made by us, all of which are cast according to our new *American System of Interchangeable Type Bodies*.

MARDER, LUSE & CO.

Announcement of the system as published by ML&Co. in 1879.

Business Booms at Foundry

They did not have to wait long. In November, 1879, three additional foundry casters were put into operation because of increased demand. "Twenty-six machines in all and Muller [is] howling for more," Luse reported.[12] By April of the next year, another machine had been added.[13] By October, 1880, Luse reported:

> Our four new steamers are about done, giving us 34 machines, and we shall build several more so that we can load you down with stock.[14]

This letter most likely had been written in response to Hawks' complaint of lack of type stock on the West Coast.

Until that time, a typefounder generally did the bulk of his business in his home town. It has been said that the demands of a large newpspaper could keep a typefoundry going singlehandedly. The increased scope of operations for ML&Co. indicated its pioneering effort was catching on far and wide. Luse wrote, "You can scarcely imagine the greatness of the field we get orders from. Today orders from Texas, Georgia, Ohio, Colorado, etc."[15] Later that month he gleefully reported having completely outfitted the *New Orleans Times*.[16]

The new system of type bodies was so well accepted that the firm discontinued its old bodies completely in July, 1880.[17] From then on, old bodies were cast only on special sorts orders.[18]

---

[12]Ibid., November 21, 1879.   [13]Ibid., April 30, 1880.
[14]Ibid., October 28, 1880.   [15]Ibid., October 10, 1880.
[16]Ibid., October 28, 1880.
[17]James Eckman, "The Chicago Type Foundry of Marder, Luse & Company, 1863-1892," *Printing and Graphic Arts,* 7:3 (September, 1959), 77.
[18]"O. B. and N. B.," *The Pacific Specimen,* 5:4 (Fourth Quarter, 1880), 5.

No doubt, Hawks was greatly pleased, making this comment later in 1880:

> The effect of our New System of type bodies on the printing craft of the United States has been just as we expected, only more so. . . . With such a general recognition of our enterprise, and full appreciation of its benefits, we can afford to let our distanced competitors howl at us and abuse us liberally.[19]

Printers, harassed by long years of justifying different sizes of type with leads, pieces of paper and whatever else could be found, kept the foundry buzzing with increasing demands for types "on the system."

Hawks Leaves ML&Co.

During this time, Hawks had been having difficulties with John Marder over outside financial dealings and other matters. Finally, he agreed in 1882 to sell his share of the partnership in Marder, Luse and Company, and strike out on other ventures and promote his "system." Subsequent travel enabled him to convince other founders they should adopt the system. First was the Cincinnati Type Foundry, where he convinced an old-time friend, Charles Wells, of the system's merit. "When my plan of the new system was submitted to him, he gave it thorough study, and quietly said: 'This is the only proper way to make type, and we will get this system underway at once.'"[20]

After violent negative reaction from James Conner at his foundry in New York, the idea began to work again. Finally (Hawks reports), Conner submitted by

---

[19]Ibid.

[20]Nelson C. Hawks, "How the Point System Was Started," *Printing Art,* 36:5 (January, 1921), 391.

saying, "It's a fool proposition, but if Charlie Wells has the nerve to grab hold of such a thing, I can, by thunder!"[21]

John K. Rogers of the Boston Type Foundry was next to seek standards for the new bodies,[22] but perhaps the greatest moving force behind the spread of the system was the Pica on which it was based—the Pica of the MacKellar, Smiths and Jordan foundry.

> The introduction of the point system was effected with astonishing rapidity. The printers were keen for it. One of the factors aiding this success, perhaps more than any other, was the fact of MacKellar, Smiths and Jordan finding itself, without great cost, a part of the reform, owing to the adoption of its Pica as the standard. All of its types on Nonpareil, Pica, Great Primer, Double Pica, Three-line Pica, etc., were immediately available in complete outfits.[23]

By 1884 six founders had taken up the system,[24] but spread of the system was not without vicious resistance. Marder, Luse & Company's home-town competition, Barnhart Brothers and Spindler, vigorously objected in 1885, noting that there were already "half a dozen systems of type bodies in the United States." Nevertheless, BB&S was to be among 16 foundries which had taken on the new system one year later.[25] Others included MacKellar, Smiths & Jordan in Philadelphia, the St. Louis Type Foundry, the Cleveland Type Foundry, and

---

[21] Ibid.

[22] Nelson C. Hawks, "The Point System, Ancient and Modern" *Inland Printer* 41:3 (December, 1923), 467.

[23] Henry Lewis Bullen, "Nelson C. Hawks' 'Invention' of the American Point System," *Inland Printer* 46:11 (August, 1929), 66.

[24] "Hawks's Aliquot System of Bodies," *Pacific Printer, Stationer and Lithographer,* 8:6 (June, 1884), 11.

[25] James Eckman, "The Great Western Type Foundry of Barnhart Brothers & Spindler, 1869-1933," *Printing and Graphic Arts,* 9:1 (March, 1961), 10.

one of the system's greatest advocates, the Central Type
Foundry of St. Louis.[26]

Founders Association Reviews System

Indeed, by this time the matter no longer could be
ignored by the United States Type Founders' Association. A three-man "Committee on Uniform Type
Bodies" was appointed to study the matter and make
recommendations. Perhaps coincidentally, the foundries represented by the three men, Carl Schraubstadter
of St. Louis' Central Type Foundry, W. P. Hunt of the
Cincinnati Type Foundry, and H. H. Thorp of the Cleveland Type Foundry, all previously had adopted the point
system.[27]

By the time the committee was appointed, the point
system already was generally accepted and in use at most
of the country's major foundries. Thus, the committee
failed even to mention the point system in its recommendations to the Association; the report adopted in
1886 concerned itself only with the size of the Pica which
should serve as the basis for the system.[28]

Majority Adopt System

Only 13 years after Marder, Luse and Company
introduced the system, a majority of the founders in the
United States had adopted the system and the standard
Pica on which it was based. Estimates of the cost of
changeover are placed at near $100,000 for new molds

---

[26]"Uniformity in Type Bodies," *Price List of Type and Printing Material* . . . (St.
Louis: Central Type Foundry, April, 1886), 3.

[27]*Proceedings of the Fifteenth Meeting of the Type Founders' Assoication of the U. S.*,
Held at Spencer House, Niagara Falls, N. Y., September 16, 1886.

[28]Ibid.

at each foundry alone.[29] Total cost to the industry, including re-alignment of existing matrices, discarding "bastard" fonts in stock, and making new molds, was estimated at near $9,000,000 by one founder.[30]

The 24 members of the United States Typefounders' Association having agreed upon the point system by 1890 were:

A. Foreman & Son, San Francisco	Illinois Typefounding Co., Chicago
Allison & Smith, Cincinnati	James Conner's Sons, New York
Barnhart Bros. & Spindler, Chicago	John G. Mengel & Co., Baltimore
Benton, Waldo & Co., Milwaukee	John T. Reton & Son, Kansas City, Mo.
Boston Typefoundry, Boston	L. Pelouse & Co., Philadelphia
Central Typefoundry, St. Louis	Marder, Luse & Co., Chicago
Cincinnati Typefoundry, Cincinnati	Palmer & Rey, San Francisco
C. J. Cary & Co., Baltimore	Phelps, Dalton & Co., Boston
Collins & McLeester, Philadelphia	St. Louis Typefoundry, St. Louis
Curtis & Mitchell, Boston	John Ryan Company, Baltimore
Farmer, Little & Co., New York	MacKellar, Smiths & Jordan Co., Phila.
H. H. Thorp Mfg. Co., Cleveland	Union Type Foundry, Chicago[31]

Marder, Luse and Company had predicted that no foundry would be able to pirate the system, but that prediction proved to be grossly untrue. The firm's competitive advantage created by the system soon was erased to the point of causing its advertising to take a rather defensive stance by 1889:

> We beg to remind our friends that having been the originators, in 1872[32], of the American System of Interchangeable Type Bodies (also known as the Point System), which was adopted by the Type Founders' Association of the

---

[29]"Standard Measurement," *Inland Printer,* 2:5 (February, 1885), 211.

[30]Hawks, "How the Point System Was Started," op. cit.

[31]"Uniformity in Type Bodies," *Inland Printer,* 8:1 (October, 1890), 73.

[32]Marder, Luse and Company, from the beginning of its point system advertising, dates the system's origin to 1872. The scheme did use some of the bodies adopted in 1872; however, the complete scheme was not conceived until 1877. This matter is documented early in this chapter.

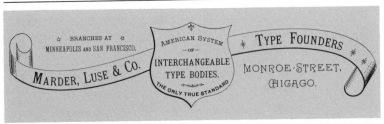

This logotype appeared in most Marder, Luse & Co., advertising after inception of the so-called "American System."

United States, on Sept. 17, 1886, we have no type to dispose of that is not cast on this system, and caution you against buying type on old bodies from founders who have but lately been compelled to adopt the point system, and have, in consequence, a large stock of type on bastard bodies, which they are willing to sell at a larger discount.[33]

Organization of American Type Founders

The old bodies which founders had been using quickly became dead weight on their stockroom shelves as printers insisted on point system bodies. The statement printed above by ML&Co. gives indication of the chaotic conditions within the industry as founders attempted to dispose of their old types while converting to the point system.

Although prices, discounts and the like were regulated by the Type Founders' Association, various founders violated rules by offering greater discounts. Once unique with a single foundry, the point system quickly became the standard of the industry. Types from different foundries could be interchanged easily, as could equipment and implements in different found-

---

[33]"35% Discount," (advertisement), *Inland Printer*, 6:8 (May, 1889), 702.

ries. These factors were to enable an even more striking change in typefounding in 1892 with the formation of the American Type Founders Company. Twenty-three founders merged to form ATF (leaving only four independents).[34] Economic considerations which were brought largely by the introduction of Linotypes and other mechanical typecasting systems no doubt played an important role, yet as the *Inland Printer* commented at the time, "It is an interesting fact that such a combination as the new company would have been impossible but for the adoption of a universal standard of type bodies like the point system."[35]

---

[34]"American Typefounders Company," *Inland Printer,* 10:2 (November, 1892), 150.

[35]"American Typefounders Company," *Inland Printer,* 10:5 (February, 1893), 394.

Chapter Five

Role of Nelson C. Hawks

EW HISTORIANS have given Nelson C. Hawks mention in relation to the introduction of the point system. Those who have mentioned him have had difficulty finding the proper place for him in their accounts. This is because the basics of the American point system are precisely the same as Fournier's, invented in 1724 (See Chapter 1).

Hawks cannot be given full credit for coming up with the idea, even though he insisted he actually devised his point system without knowledge of Fournier's. Hawks' position in history is still quite important, however, for he was personally responsible for the system's initial adoption by Marder, Luse and Company. Later, he also was responsible for getting the system into the minds of other founders, and is responsible for convincing them of its practical merit.

Practical Printer

Hawks considered himself a practical printer rather than a typefounder, although he practiced both professions at various times during his life. Born in Milwaukee, Wisconsin, August 21, 1840, Nelson Crocker Hawks was the son of an influential pioneer family in the early days of the state. His family moved to Delafield, not far from Milwaukee, shortly after he was born. There his father built a flowering mill, erected a hotel, and a store.

Hawks was educated in the common schools of
Delafield, and at the early age of 11 was seized with a
desire to learn the printer's trade. His father resisted, but
finally allowed his son, at the age of 16, to work as a
printer's devil at the Waukesha *Plaindealer*. This association lasted only one month because the newspaper was
sold. The former employer, a Mr. Pratt, sympathized
with young Hawks' ambition to become a printer, and
made a gift of 27 pounds of old Long Primer type.[1]

Shortly, Hawks began a newspaper which he called
Young America, using the old type and makeshift equipment. At 18, with more elaborate equipment, he began
publication of the *Free Press* at Oconomowoc, which continued in publication for many years after he left the
state.

In 1865 he moved to Milwaukee, where he engaged
in job printing, shortly afterwards taking as a partner
Norman L. Burdick. This partnership continued until
1874 when John Marder induced Hawks to sell his share
of the partnership to Burdick and join Marder, Luse and
Company to open and manage the foundry's new San
Francisco agency.[2]

No Knowledge of Fournier

Hawks' early background, therefore, was entirely in
the areas of job printing and newspaper publication. His
early activities, his schooling, and his memoirs many
years after introduction of the point system indicate he
was not what one might call a "printing scholar." There-

[1]William E. Loy, "Typefounders and Typefounding in America No. XXVIII:
Nelson Crocker Hawks," *Inland Printer*, 23:2 (November, 1902), 249.
[2]Ibid.

fore, his description of how he arrived at his idea for units in the point system—by counting the sizes from Nonpareil to Pica — seems quite plausible. Hawks explains:

> When I studied out my plan in 1877 I had never heard of Fournier or of Didot, and did not learn what the Fournier system was until many years afterward, when Henry L. Bullen sent me the Fournier book. Therefore, the idea was as original with me as it was with him. It serves as corroborating proof that there is only one proper way to make type.[3]

Hawks' statement that he did not know of the Fournier system is substantiated by an "explanation" published in 1889 by the Hawks and Shattuck foundry in San Francisco, of which Nelson Hawks was a principal. By attributing origin of the French system to Didot, and by suggesting the system was based on multiples of 10, his lack of familiarity with the French system (at the time) becomes evident:

> Fractional type bodies were first introduced into France by M. Didot. The graduation was made by tenths, their 10-point body, Corpus, being the standard. The French bodies, however, not agreeing with the American inch, Mr. N. C. Hawks, of San Francisco, proposed the above plan of gradation by twelfths, from a Pica that should gauge exactly $1/6$ of an inch. . . .[4]

This is not to suggest, however, that the Fournier system was not known at the time in the United States. On the contrary, at least one general publication on printing, Ringwalt's *American Encyclopaedia of Printing*, published in 1872, discussed the Fournier system in

---

[3]Nelson C. Hawks, "The Point System, Ancient and Modern," *Inland Printer*, 44:3 (December, 1923), 467.

[4]"Explanation of the Aliquot System of Bodies," *Hawks & Shattuck's New Specimen Book* (San Francisco: Hawks & Shattuck, 1889).

great detail. Discussion therein, under the heading "Standard of Type," labored the fact that no standard existed at the time in the United States or in England, but that Fournier's system, and later Didot's, had been well established in France. An example of Ringwalt's explanation:

> ... To apply this in practice, he [Fournier] assigned to each body a definite number of Points. Thus, the body of Cicero, corresponding to our Pica, was twelve points, and it was rendered exactly of these dimensions by laying twelve Cicero types on the two-inch standard, and dressing them until they exactly fitted the required space. Nonpareil, half a Cicero, was six points. . . . Leads were made to a certain number of points; and thus any body worked with another without justification. . . .[5]

The French system, furthermore, was known in the Marder, Luse and Company foundry, as evidenced by the following mention in a lengthy discussion which dismissed the French idea in the firm's house organ, *The Chicago Specimen,* in 1870. To wit:

> The French have endeavored to regulate this matter by law; but so carelessly have the enactments been drawn that, we believe, their provisions are frequently evaded. The plan intended there to be followed is to make the type conform to certain Typographic Points, or 72nd parts of an inch. This is the usual variation between Pica and Small Pica in this country, which as we have before shown, will not answer for the smaller sizes.[6]

John Marder most likely wrote the comment above, for correspondence between A. P. Luse and Nelson

---

[5]J. Luther Ringwalt, ed., *American Encyclopaedia of Printing* (Philadelphia: Menamin and Ringwalt, 1871), 471.

[6]"Gossip with Correspondents and Readers," *The Chicago Specimen,* 4:4 (October, 1870), 4.

Hawks during that time period indicates production of *The Chicago Specimen* generally was left to Marder. In 1870, therefore, Marder was dismissing the 12-points-to-Pica idea as completely impractical.

Marder insisted on thinking of type sizes as they *were*, arguing that it would be unthinkable to alter the size of smaller types to conform to such a system because printers would not tolerate such drastic size changes. (Keep in mind that no size would be changed as much as one point, for sizes in the Fournier system went by one-point increments from six to twelve points.)

Practical Printer's Idea

Hawks, on the other hand, had found himself in the midst of mis-matched fonts from different foundries on many occasions during his life. His idea was developed because he had a great sense of need for such a system.

It has remained for a practical printer, one who has 'been there' and seen the waste of time, to formulate a thorough system that answers the purpose in all particulars. This system is ... graded with mathematical precision, so that a printer in making justification of two or more sizes of letter, rule, etc., will not have to go by rule of thumb and "feel for even," and shut one eye and *look* for lining. NO; all this guessing, looking and feeling is done away with, and it is instead we have a rule—a practical scale to justify by, when these bodies are used.[7]

Henry L. Bullen Credits Hawks

Did Hawks invent the system? Henry L. Bullen, widely published authority on printing subjects in the early 1900's and founder and developer of the

---

[7]"The Fractional System," *Pacific Printer, Stationer & Lithographer,* 7:1 (January, 1883), 10.

Typographic Library and Museum of the American Type Founders Company, says yes.

> It is my carefully considered opinion that Nelson C. Hawks, quite unaware of Fournier's invention, actually did himself "invent" the American point system, and that the exact similarity in principle of both systems is merely a remarkable coincidence. I base this opinion upon knowledge of Hawks' integrity. Coincidences like this are not infrequent. It is a well-known truth that photolithography was invented and patented almost simultaneously in the same year by a man in Melbourne, Australia, and another man in St. Petersburg, Russia, neither having knowledge of the other's activities.[8]

Academic arguments in trade publications or encyclopedias, nor the efforts of several individuals prior to this time, however, failed to do what Nelson C. Hawks did manage. He convinced a typefounder to accept and implement the proposition. This was in 1877 when he convinced John Marder that the system *was* practical, and when Marder carried the idea back to the Chicago foundry and sold the idea to Carl Muller and A. P. Luse, the other partners in the firm.

Fournier's system may have been known and discussed during this period in America. But there is no indication that it was seriously considered as a standard for the country. After ML&Co.'s introduction of the system, however, competitors often sought to discredit the foundry's claim to origin of the system. Barnhart Brothers & Spindler, for example, noted in 1889 that "the system now known as the Point System . . . is simply an adaptation . . . of the French Point System, which has

---

[8]Henry L. Bullen, "Nelson C. Hawks' 'Invention' of the American Point System," *Inland Printer*, 46:11 (August, 1929), 65.

Nelson Crocker Hawks
Original illustration accompanied his article in Printing Art *magazine.*

been in use in France more than 100 years. . . ."[9]
Barnhart Brothers labeled ML&Co.'s claim "misleading" and an "advertising dodge."

Trouble in Partnership

Hawks' "logical" plan for the point system, perhaps, was not representative of his efficiency in running the San Francisco branch for Marder, Luse and Company. As early as 1876, A. P. Luse noted in a letter to Hawks:

"We are constantly getting mixed on your orders. You seem to make repetitions and duplicate orders and then your orders often are not plain."[10] Two years later the matter still was not remedied, as evidenced by Luse's stern instructions: "What we want is a positive and specific order for what you must have."[11]

The branch, nevertheless, grew to the point where typecasting facilities were installed in San Francisco. To help in this endeavor, John Stover, a nephew of John Marder, who had worked in the Chicago foundry for eight years, was sent to San Francisco. Luse wrote in July, 1878, that Stover was "well posted and thoroughly reliable."[12] Then a month later, he changed his tune somewhat by saying, "John is coming in three weeks. You must not expect too much of John. He is a good worker but doesn't know much about business."[13]

During the same period, John Marder was stricken with serious illness which kept him away from the foun-

---

[9]James Eckman, "The Great Western Type Foundry of Barnhart Brothers and Spindler, 1869-1933," *Printing and Graphic Arts*, 9:1 (March, 1961), 11.

[10]A. P. Luse, personal letter to N. C. Hawks, March 4, 1876.

[11]A. P. Luse, personal letter to N. C. Hawks, August 26, 1878.

[12]A. P. Luse, personal letter to N. C. Hawks, July 26, 1878.

[13]A. P. Luse, personal letter to N. C. Hawks, August 30, 1878.

dry for over a year. Hawks had visited Chicago in 1878. Luse wrote in September, 1879, that "Mr. M. has given me but little help for a long time—not since you were here."[14]

From the outset, Hawks had difficulty with Stover. He wrote Luse concerning Stover's inability to shoulder part of the responsibility for running the San Francisco operation, and finally, the two agreed it would be best to terminate Stover's employment. Marder, who had not been active in the organization during these months, regained his health and resumed active participation just about the time Stover was dismissed. As Hawks related in his personal journal:

> This annoyed Mr. Marder so much I didn't get a pleasant letter from him all that year. A misunderstanding about our trade, too, made matters worse. John carried lots of tales East too, and poisoned Mr. Marder against me.[15]

The "trade" Hawks referred to concerned the sale of his father's homestead and brother's farm in Wisconsin for a larger share of interest in the San Francisco branch. Hawks had visions of developing the land into a resort, centering around a natural spring on the property. This idea was pursued on a limited scale. But Luse reached this conclusion early in 1881:

> The fact is the land is a perfect sink hole for money and it has already swallowed up $2,000 clean cash and its jaws are still as wide open as the bed and platen of a Liberty press.[16]

From this point on, matters continued to deteriorate in the partnership. Relationships between Luse and

---

[14]A. P. Luse, personal letter to N. C. Hawks, September 9, 1879.

[15]This is an entry in Hawks' personal journal. It is not dated. The journal is now preserved in the Kemble Collections, California Historical Society.

[16]A. P. Luse, personal letter to N. C. Hawks, January 18, 1881.

Marder also were strained to the point where Luse wrote, February 4, 1882, that Hawks was taken into the organization with his "scarecely being consulted," and that he would help Hawks in every way to get out of the partnership. Then he added that he too would welcome the opportunity to get out of the partnership "at figures much below the balance sheet exhibit."[17]

The same month, Marder wrote Hawks: "I am under no obligation to anyone to prolong the partnership in San Francisco and it is my desire to have it closed up as speedily as possible.[18]

Hawks Sells Out

Luse went to California that same month, where an agreement was signed stating that Hawks would sell out for $12,000, and would give control of the property in Wisconsin to Luse.[19] The new San Francisco manager was to be Hugh Wells, who took over April 1, 1882.[20]

Then the matter became public scandal when Marder, Luse and Company entered a suit against Hawks for $790.38, which was an amount ML&Co. claimed Hawks took from the branch operation after the partnership had terminated. The matter first was discussed in *The Pacific Printer,* published by Palmer and Rey, a competitor and San Francisco agent for the Miller and Richard typefoundry of Edinburgh, Scotland. "A Disgraceful Suit" was the title of the article. Then, Marder, Luse and Company spread its side of the story

---

[17]A. P. Luse, personal letter to N. C. Hawks, February 4, 1882.

[18]John Marder, personal letter to N. C. Hawks, February 22, 1882.

[19]Printed copy of a draft agreement, February 27, 1882, signed by A. P. Luse and N. C. Hawks in San Jose, California.

[20]"Change in Firm," *The Pacific Specimen,* 6:4 (Fourth Quarter, 1881), 1.

in a four-page flier giving full details of the matter and claiming it had become "painfully apparent to all concerned that Nelson C. Hawks was not competent to manage the business.[21]

Obviously, Hawks' final departure was anything but "friendly." In later years, this disagreement caused Hawks to receive little, if any, credit for the original idea of the point system. Indeed, John Marder, on at least one occasion, took full credit for the idea. This involved an article in *The Neat Printer,* published by the Cranston Press, San Antonio, Texas. Its December, 1886, issue featured a large portrait of John Marder, with this statement:

> *The Neat Printer* has already published a description of the Interchangeable System, and it is pleased to present in this issue a portrait of its originator, John Marder, the printers' friend.[22]

Hawks Spreads the Idea

No longer associated with ML&Co., Hawks now felt no compulsion to help that firm maintain its monopoly on the point system. It was then that he ventured to Cincinnati and New York to promote the system. There, as related in Chapter 4, he was able to induce other founders to adopt the system. Returning West, Hawks became associated with his former competitor in San Francisco, the Palmer and Rey foundry. They adopted the new system and labeled it the "Hawks's Aliquot System of Bodies."[23]

---

[21]A four-page flier produced by Marder, Luse and Company entitled "Marder, Luse & Co. vs. N. C. Hawks." Undated.

[22]"The Printer's Friend," *The Neat Printer,* 1:3 (December, 1886), 1.

[23]"Hawks's Aliquot System of Bodies," *Pacific Printer, Stationer & Lithographer,* 8:6 (June, 1884), 11.

N. J. Werner, a typefounder from St. Louis during that time, notes the Central Type Foundry of that city, operated by James A. St. John and Carl G. Schraubstadter, was "the great push that finally put the idea of point system types into a going proposition. The inventor of the American point system [he named Hawks] had a difficult time of it, trying to induce the foundries to adopt it. He got small and desultory action from one or two concerns. Concerted action came, however, when the Central Foundry announced that it would adopt point system bodies. Whereupon, all the other then-existing foundries couldn't follow the leader fast enough."[24]

Hawks' vigorous activity in promoting the point system was ample reason for Henry L. Bullen to label him "undoubtedly the John the Baptist of the gospel of the point system in America."[25] Hawks' activity was a most significant factor in the quick adoption of the system throughout the typefounding industry. William E. Loy, who wrote biographies of many typefounders for the *Inland Printer*, notes that the point system "owes much to the persistence of N. C. Hawks."[26]

About 1886, after his contract with Palmer and Rey had expired, Hawks became the San Francisco agent for the Conner typefoundry of New York, and the Barnhart Brothers & Spindler foundry of Chicago.[27] He was induced to part with half interest in his business by William

---

[24]N. J. Werner, "An Address by N. J. Werner, 'Originator of Standard Type Alignment,' " before the St. Louis Club of Printing House Craftsmen. (A printed copy of the address is preserved in the ATF Collection at Columbia University, dated "after 1928" by H. L. Bullen in a note inside the cover.)

[25]Bullen, op. cit.   [26]Loy, op cit.   [27]Ibid.

F. Shattuck; shortly thereafter, the enlarged firm began the manufacture of type in a small way. The firm grew, manufacturing under the name Hawks and Shattuck's Pacific States Type Foundry, until 1892, when the business was incorporated. Shattuck then took a larger share in the business.[28]

Hawks Honored at ATF Formation

That same year, American Type Founders was formed, being a merger of 23 different foundries. At an organizational banquet in New York City, Hawks was honored in a speech made by William Bright of the St. Louis Type Foundry.

> There is a man sitting at this table who deserves a scoring at our hands, as a body of American founders, for he is the cause of our clear loss of over nine millions of dollars, in the discarding of old moulds alone. I allude to the so-called point system. But I tell you, gentlemen, it is the grandest thing that has ever happened to typography, and marks a new era in the history of printing.[29]

In 1894, Hawks sold his remaining interest in the Pacific States Type Foundry to Shattuck.[30] Thereafter, he turned from typefounding and ventured into the photographic supply business. In 1910, perhaps motivated by John Marder's annoying claim to authorship of the point system, Hawks wrote this poem to Henry L. Bullen:

> *Today I reached the span of life—my three score years and ten.*
> *I'm wondering if my name appears among the list of men*

---

[28]Ibid.

[29]N. C. Hawks, "How the Point System was Started," *Printing Art*, 36:5 (January, 1921), 392.

[30]"Trade Notes," *Inland Printer*, 12:6 (March, 1894), 508.

In the Typographic History of the Century just passed—
The printers and the men by whom their little types were cast.

In humble way those men were great, and we will surely find
That truthful records will prevail, and falsehood leave
*   behind*
For they created power that made the world progress
Through that Archimedian lever, the Glorious Printing
*   Press.* [31]

Hawks lived to see his system become the standard of the entire English-speaking world. At 80, he noted, "The only benefit I have derived from it lies in the satisfaction of having been successful in giving the printing craft something useful and lasting."[32] He died at Alameda, California, July 2, 1929, at the age of 89.[33]

---

[31]N. C. Hawks, personal letter to H. L. Bullen, August 21, 1912.

[32]N. C. Hawks, "How the Point System was Started," *Printing Art*, 36:5 (January, 1921), 392.

[33]"Nelson C. Hawks (obituary)," *Pacific Printer*, 42:1 (July, 1929), 53.

Chapter Six

The Size of Pica

AFTER IT HAD BECOME clearly evident that Hawks' 12-points-to-the-Pica idea was to take over the typefounding industry, those reluctant to adopt the system raised considerable argument over the fact that the precise size of the Pica still was in question—that, indeed, there were at least two Picas being used by founders as "standard." One measured precisely one-sixth of an inch. The other was the so-called "Johnson" Pica.

The Johnson Pica

The Johnson Pica was named for Lawrence Johnson, who operated the L. Johnson typefoundry in Philadelphia. The foundry was direct successor to Binny and Ronaldson, the nation's oldest successful foundry. When Johnson died in 1860, his three junior partners, Thomas MacKellar, J. F. Smith, Richard Smith, and a fourth person, P. A. Jordan, purchased his interest in the business and it came to be known as MacKellar, Smiths and Jordan.[1] This firm's Pica measured .1660 inch, six Picas coming to only .996 inch.[2] It was by far the most popular Pica in the typefounding industry. Even before the point system was first considered, the Johnson Pica served as the standard for Marder, Luse and Company,

---

[1] William M. Patton, "Thomas MacKellar," *Official Souvenir, Eighth Annual Convention of the United Typothetae of America,* (1894), 31.

[2] "Answers to Correspondence," *Inland Printer,* 3:12 (September, 1886), 771.

Chicago; Farmer, Little and Company, New York; and the Cleveland Type Foundry, in addition to MacKellar, Smiths and Jordan.[3]

Marder, Luse and Company adopted the Johnson Pica when the foundry was re-built after the Chicago fire of 1871. Perhaps this was done because "the job types and borders of that [MS&J] foundry were in most general use."[4] Rather than re-make all its molds when adopting Hawks' system six years later, the foundry retained its Pica mold, its Nonpareil, Double-Pica, Four-Line Pica, and certain others, which had been made to work as exact multiples of each other when the foundry was rebuilt after the Chicago fire.[5] Thus, the Pica on which the point system was established proved to be something short of an even sixth of an inch.

Hawks Tries for Sixth of Inch

Nelson Hawks himself, after his break with Marder, Luse and Company in 1882, made an effort to correct this discrepancy. The firm with which he was next associated, Palmer and Rey of San Francisco, boasting of its newly adopted "Hawks's Aliquot System of Bodies," adopted a Pica sized exactly one-sixth of an inch. To do battle with Marder, Luse and Company, Palmer and Rey matched four eight-inch settings of Pica type "on the point system" in their July, 1884, *Pacific Printer, Stationer & Lithographer.* Specimens came from James Conner's Sons of New York, the Cincinnati Type Foundry, Palmer

---

[3]"Touching-up the Typefounders," *British & Colonial Printer & Stationer,* 31:3 (January 19, 1893), 2.

[4]Henry L. Bullen, "Nelson C. Hawks' 'Invention' of the American Point System," *Inland Printer,* 49:11 (August, 1929), 70.

[5]"O. B. and N. B." *Pacific Specimen,* 5:4 (Fourth Quarter, 1880), 5.

and Rey, and Marder, Luse and Company. The article boastfully noted all specimens came precisely to the eight-inch mark with the exception of ML&Co., which fell a quarter Pica short.[6]

What the article failed to point out, however, was that these were the only three founders using a Pica of precisely one-sixth of an inch, out of the dozen or so which had adopted the point system at that time.[7]

Formation of the Type Founders' Association

There had been a phenomenal increase in the number of type foundries after the invention in the 1840's of the process of making matrices by electrotyping existing type fonts. With more foundries vying for business, cut-throat competition evolved. To protect typefounders from each other, the Type Founders' Association of the United States was established in 1864, starting with 22 charter members. One of the principal points in the group's constitution was Article IV, which read:

> Every Type-Founder who becomes a member binds himself, on his honour, to observe and carry out faithfully the prices and terms of sale agreed upon by the Association.[8]

As the years passed, various matters relating to fair business practices came before the group. It was inevitable that the question of type bodies would come up. When the matter arose, a "Committee on Uniform Type Bodies" was established, and its report was given at the

---

[6]"Caution," *The Pacific Printer, Stationer & Lithographer,* 8:7 (July, 1884), 9.

[7]*Price List of Type and Printing Material* (St. Louis: Central Type Foundry, April, 1886).

[8]Type Founders Association of the United States, *Constitution.* Adopted January 20-21, 1864, Astor House, New York City.

fifteenth meeting of the group, September 16, 1886, at
Niagara Falls, New York. The 16 founders present heard
the following report:

> Your committee respectfully recommends that the so-called
> Johnson Pica and "height" to paper be adopted as the official
> standard of the Type Founders' Association.[9]

"Mr. MacKellar[10] moved its approval. It was
approved."[11] This short paragraph established the standard which remains even today.

It is significant to note that the resolution made no
mention of the point system, although it often is assumed that at this meeting the point system, specifically,
was adopted.

Johnson Standard Defined

For a precise definition of this Pica and height standard, then, one must consult the MacKellar foundry.
Mathematical descriptions of the foundry's standards
were given in the company's *Typographic Advertiser*, in the
Spring of 1885:

> For the bodies of our foundry we use a standard of steel rod
> 35 centimeters long, which is divided in 83 parts, each part
> being equal to a Pica body, and the twelfth part of Pica (called
> a point) is the unit by which we measure our type. This steel
> rod serves also as a standard for the height to paper, which
> being 2⅓ centimeters, makes 15 type-heights equal to 35
> centimeters.[12]

---

[9]*Proceedings* of the Fifteenth Meeting of the Type Founders' Association of the
United States. Held September 16, 1886, Spencer House, Niagara Falls, New
York.

[10]Thomas MacKellar was president of the Type Founders' Association at the
time. As president, he could not make the motion. Thus, his son, William B.
MacKellar, also a member of the Association and present at the Niagara Falls
meeting, probably made the motion.

[11]*Proceedings,* op. cit.

[12]"Uniform Type-Bodies," The MacKellar, Smiths & Jordan Co.'s *Typographic
Advertiser,* 31:117 (Springtime, 1885).

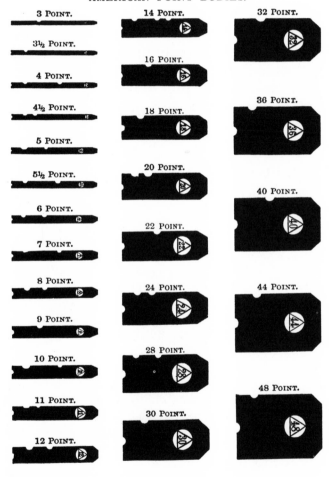

*A size scale showing point bodies printed originally
by MacKellar, Smiths and Jordan.*

Four years after the Type Founders' agreement, the United Typothetae of America (which became Printing Industries of America in 1945) appointed a committee to consider the subject of a possible greater uniformity in the bodies of types from different foundries. The committee contacted every typefounder in the United States in an effort to discover precisely why the Johnson Pica had been adopted in preference to the larger one measuring a sixth of an inch, or, indeed, the Didot point, which by then had been accepted by European typefounders. From the report, published in 1890:

United Typothetae Reviews Situation

The first attempt at uniformity by means of points began with the theory that the Pica should be one-sixth of the American inch, and that there should be twelve points to the Pica. This method of making a basis was not approved by the founders whose Pica was less than one-sixth of an inch, and these founders were in the majority. It was finally decided that the standard Pica should be the Pica of the MacKellar, Smiths & Jordan Company. It was claimed by the advocates of this standard that this body of Pica, made by the oldest foundry in the United States, had already been adopted by many other founders, and was used by more printers than any other body of Pica; and that a system of points based on this Pica would inflict the least loss on founders and printers who had to change from the old to the new system. These conclusions were accepted reluctantly by those who had made Pica of a larger body. They objected to the new standard as capriciously and unscientifically selected, not based on any regular fraction of the foot or meter.

The need for a more definite standard than an accidentally selected Pica led to the discovery that 83 Picas of the accepted body were equal to 35 centimeters. It was also found that by making a very slight alteration in the height that 35 centimeters would exactly meet 15 heights of type. The old standard of height was eleven-twelfths or $^{916}/_{1000}$ of an inch. . . .

Your committee have [sic] also been asked why the United States Typefounders' Association did not accept the point system which now prevails in Europe, generally known in France and southern Europe as the Didot system, and in Germany as the Berthold system. The Didot system was intelligently considered, but was rejected for good cause. The Didot point is too great. The adoption of the Didot point would have compelled the retirement not only of all existing molds and matrices, but would have required the recutting of new punches for too many sizes. The point adopted by the United States Typefounders' Association is .0351 centimeters. This is almost identical with the point devised in 1737 by Fournier le jeune, of Paris, the true inventor of the point system. The point substituted afterward by Ambroise-Firmin Didot is .0376 centimeters. Eleven points of the Didot system are almost as large as twelve points of the American system. French typographers of the highest authority have recorded their regret at the change in size from the Fournier to the Didot point. Sharing this belief we think the United States Typefounders' Association acted wisely in preferring that system which allows of nicer subdivision and does not materially disturb existing sizes. . . .[13]

The committee report listed 24 foundries which had agreed upon the point system and had actually instituted the reform by 1890. Each had undergone tremendous expense in re-working molds and matrices in order to adopt the system. Printers also had undergone great expense in adopting point system types because they had to discard old bodies in the process. Thus, it can be safely concluded that by 1890, the point system and the Johnson Pica both were firmly established, whether

---

[13]"Uniformity in Type Bodies," *Inland Printer,* 8:1 (October, 1890), 71-73.

mathematically convenient or not, and that no further change in the system would be promoted either by typefounders or printers.

Fournier and American Picas Related

It is with more than passing interest that Theodore L. DeVinne (who was a member of the committee which prepared the report just noted) in his book, *The Practice of Typography: A Treatise on Plain Printing Types,* declares the close similarity of the Fournier Pica and the Johnson Pica was more than a coincidence. The difference amounts to only four points in the standard 35 centimeter measure.

It is possible that the American system, based on the Pica of the MacKellar, Smiths & Jordan Co., was unwittingly derived from Fournier. Thomas says, in his *History of Printing in America* (vol. I, p. 29, second edition), that Benjamin Franklin purchased of P. S. Fournier "the materials of an old foundry," and had his grandson, B. F. Bache, instructed in the art by Fournier, with intent to establish an extensive foundry in Philadelphia. The foundry so established did not thrive: it was neglected and abandoned by Bache, but after Franklin's death the typefounding tools became the property of his relative, Duane, who kindly offered to lend them all to Binny & Ronaldson, then the only founders of importance in that city. Ronaldson was struck with their superiority, and fearing that Duane might change his mind at once got a wheelbarrow and trundled them to his own foundry. Binny acknowledged that he received many valuable suggestions from these tools.

With this testimony as to the value of the tools, added to our knowledge of Franklin's interest in scientific instruments of every kind, it may be assumed that Fournier sold not old but new tools, and that he had provided everything needed to establish his point system in America, in the equipment which he furnished Bache. There can be no doubt that Binny &

Ronaldson had, and made use of, the Fournier mold for Pica, and that the standard they fixed for this body was accepted by their successors, L. Johnson & Co. and the MacKellar, Smiths & Jordan Co. The slight deviation from the Fournier mold for four points in one thousand may be accepted as the consequence of untended and gradually imperceptible changes which would occur after a long use of the molds in early days.[14]

Mathematical Explanation

Perhaps further reason for the Pica to be sized as it is relates to mathematics.[15] Students of mathematics are aware of the infinite fraction "left over" when whole items are subdivided by three, six or 12. Such is the case with the inch, the sixth part equaling .1666666⅔. This infinitely recurring fraction was eliminated with the Johnson Pica so six Picas came up four thousandths short of the full inch. Thus, 72 Picas are short of one foot by about 3½ points.[16]

One author argues that the committee which met at Niagara Falls in 1886 "attached greater importance to deciding the size of the 'Pica' . . . than to deciding the size of the 'point.'"[17] (The point, being the twelfth part of the Pica, was still plagued with the problem of a recurring fraction.) He failed to realize, however, that the Committee did not consider the unit now known as the point. Its main objective (and quite a formidable one) was to estab-

[14]Theodore L. DeVinne, *The Practice of Typography: A Treatise on the Process of Type-Making, the Point System, the Names, Sizes, Styles and Prices of Plain Printing Types* (2d ed.: New York: The Century Press, 1902), 155.

[15]*Useful Matrix Information,* published in 1937 by the Mergenthaler Linotype Company, plainly states the recurring fraction was its reason for adopting the Pica measuring .1660 inch. Mergenthaler also notes that its point is .0383 inch.

[16]"Answers to Correspondents," op. cit.

[17]R. C. Elliott, "The Development of the 'Point' Unit of Type Measurement," *The Monotype Recorder,* 30:241 (1931), 17.

lish a "standard"—something all English-speaking printers had labored without for over 400 years. This "standard" was judged to be the ancient and well-known Pica
rather than the newly introduced unit called the point.

This accomplishment should not be ridiculed merely
because it appears to be inadequate today in the fourth
decimal place. Founders then were working with type
bodies cast in metal, subject to problems of expansion
and contraction of metals in casting, heat of the molds,
etc. Once the types were in the printers' shops, the dirt of
everyday use quickly altered their micrometric sizes.
Thus, matters relating to the fourth and fifth decimal
places were of much less significance in 1886 than today,
where electronic and photographic composition have
become a way of life.

Chapter Seven

Extension of the Point System

ADOPTION of the point system by Marder, Luse and Company in 1877 was only the first step toward the standardization in type manufacture which was eventually to make the products of different type foundries interchangeable. Success of typesetting machinery such as the Linotype also hinged upon these refinements.

As founders, one by one, adopted the point system, the point was carried to dimensions never contemplated by Marder, Luse and Company. *Names* to designate sizes first were dropped, matters of alignment were standardized, and the point was used to establish point-set bodies for all characters in a font.

The restricted scope of Marder, Luse and Company's introduction is indicated by the fact that a primary concern of John Marder was obtaining trademark protection for the new *names* created by his firm to identify new sizes, and, indeed, the system's name itself.

Marder put a certain amount of study into creation of these names. This is explained as the primary reason for taking out the trademark "American System of Interchangeable Type Bodies," upon formally announcing the system in 1879.

> This has been done through no fear of attempts to pirate the system throughout, as that would be an experiment too costly for many of this class of competitor to undertake; but they

wish to be in a position to protect their customers from imposition by those who might try the less costly device of copying some of the names by which the new sizes are to be known, or adopting the name of the system itself.[1]

In a letter to Nelson Hawks on March 8, 1878, Marder said: "I propose to name them as follows: 'Norse' 1; 'Saxon' 1½; 'American' 2; 'German' 2½; 'Brilliant' 3. . . ."[2]

Later, Marder apparently re-arranged these names, making "American" stand for the one-point body. Many other names were created—thirty-one in all—for sizes from one to 72 points.

Marder wanted "American" to signify the unit on which the system was to be based. But as it is evident today, the single unit came to be known as the "point," a term which was referred to even in Marder, Luse and Company's first announcement with regard to European systems. The "point" apparently was used with increasing frequency from that time on.

Old bodies and new bodies both were in use in many printshops. Attempts to distinguish between the two only resulted in confusion. A printer complained of this in 1888:

> The absurdities following are my apology for thus addressing you. What shall we say of printers—master printers, or their foremen—who use such expressions as "12-point point slugs on the point system," "6-to-Pica brass rule, point system," and many other terms equally nonsensical and absurd, as are used by them in ordinary type, etc.? The point system of type bodies has been grossly and, in many instances, ignorantly misrepresented. If there be in the system what

---

[1]Advertisement from *The Chicago Specimen*, 13:3&4 (Third Quarter, 1879), 2.
[2]John Marder, personal letter to N. C. Hawks, March 8, 1878.

some boasters, in introducing it, and since, have claimed for it
. . . then such nonsense as above quoted could hardly be
possible. . . ."[3]

"The old names never did mean anything real," the
writer complained and therefore suggested that by
common consent, they should be abolished. The "grand
old names," as they were called affectionately, were tied
closely to all other traditions in the printshop, however,
and some typefounders refused to abandon them.

Only a year before ML&Co. introduced the point
system with its "Parallel Shaded" face, the Central Type
Foundry in St. Louis was established. Not having a great
inventory of "old body" molds and matrices on hand, the
new foundry's proprietors, James A. St. John and Carl
G. Schraubstadter, embraced the new system and promoted it vigorously.[4]

Old Names Abandoned

From the beginning, this foundry insisted on calling
the new type bodies by the number of points they measured, arguing "This nomenclature will also give the
printer a more definite and better idea as to the relative
sizes of the bodies when used either together or apart. It
is easily comprehended, being as simple as the addition
table. There never was much sense in the old names,
being merely arbitrary and capricious, and we are in
favor of abolishing them entirely."[5]

Among other early advocates of size designations in
points was the Cleveland Type Foundry, operated by

---

[3]"Sensible Suggestions," *Inland Printer,* 5:9 (June, 1888), 676.

[4]"An Address by N. J. Werner, 'Originator of Standard Type Alignment,'"
before the St. Louis Club of Printing House Craftsmen, c. 1928.

[5]"Our Type Bodies," *Price List of Type and Printing Material* (St. Louis: Central
Typefoundry, 1890), 4.

Identical type face and identical type size (the letter j). The difference: One is cast by the Conner foundry of New York on a Double Great Primer body before introduction of the point system. The second is cast by the Cincinnati Type Foundry on a 36-point body, a move which forced descending characters to kern off the bottom of the smaller body. Poor arrangements such as this were prevalent until founders were able to re-cut faces to fit point-body molds without overhangs or excessive shoulders.

H. H. Thorp Manufacturing Company.[6] It was not until 1884 that Marder, Luse and Company began identifying types in its advertising with point-size designations, and then only in parentheses after the name-size designation. Thereafter, point-size listings quickly removed the former names to their places in our history books.

Introduction of the point system brought many odd and unacceptable modifications in the physical appearance of types. One of the most unsuitable practices was using matrices made *before* introduction of the point system for casting types on point bodies. Invariably, the matrices did not fit new bodies properly. In some cases, bodies were much smaller than before, forcing the old matrices to descend off the newer point bodies.

This, and other such half-way adaptations of the point system brought very little relief to the comp. He still had to use pieces of paper and leads to obtain proper alignment of letters from differing fonts and found himself with type more fragile than before. A contemporary printer discussed the matter by explaining:

> Now, take book-work first. You have to set a catalogue, a class-book, a book of reference, or other work requiring prominent side-heads, and you start in on your nice new type on Point Bodies. Let us suppose the work is in eight-point-Brevier. The side-heads are in Antique, Latin Antique, Gothic, Bold-face Italic, or anything else, all on eight-point bodies, yet none of them and no two of them line with the same amount of justifying! How's this? Why, my dear boy, you're not kicking are you? You ordered Point *Bodies* and you got them. . . .[7]

---

[6]"The Point System," *Typographic Gazette*, 4:10 (Fall and Winter, 1887-8), 1. Published by the H. H. Thorp Manufacturing Company—Cleveland Type Foundry.

[7]George W. Bateman, "Points," *The Superior Printer*, 2:5&6 (September-October, 1888), 51.

This writer proposed that small job type have the same shoulder regardless of design, and that all other type have shoulders of established point widths so various sizes would line by the use of one- or two-point leads.

Standard Line Developed

This thought was developed in detail in 1889 by N. J. Werner in a publication entitled *Artist Printer*.[8] Werner later explained that his idea most likely would have passed into oblivion had it not been for the creation of the Inland Type Foundry in St. Louis soon thereafter. Owners of the firm, Carl, William A. and Oswald Schraubstadter, put Werner's idea into full use, calling it "Standard Line." Their first specimen book, published in 1895, featured the Standard Line idea throughout.[9]

Werner notes the firm "soon became a leader in its field, and through its showing the great practicability of standardized alignment, quickly had numerous followers. In fact, all the other founders had to fall in line. Standard Line, after capturing America, conquered England, Germany and Australia."[10]

A comment by Henry L. Bullen regarding Werner's lining system is penned in the front cover of an undated publication of an address given by Werner to the St. Louis Printing House Craftsmen:

> Much of the information is authentic. The deductions are nearly all eroneous. Werner is an able but narrow-minded man. To him, however, belongs all the credit for applying the standard lining system. . . .[11]

---

[8]N. J. Werner, address, op. cit.
[9]*Improved Type for Printers* (St. Louis: Inland Type Foundry, 1895).
[10]N. J. Werner, address, op. cit.   [11]Ibid.

THERE is "PIE" in this "PI."

HE subjoined matter consisted originally of thirty-one lines each set in a different face of STANDARD LINE type. After proving the form we "mixed it up." The words remain unchanged, their arrangement only having been altered. The first words of the thirty-one lines, however, are placed in consecutive order in the beginning of the "pied" form here printed. The length of the lines below is 35 ems of 12-Point; in the original matter their length is 27 ems 12-Point. ☛ ☛ For the First correct solution, placing the words and lines in proper order, and naming (as per names given in our sheets and books) the faces they are set in, we offer a

PRIZE OF $50

For the Second correct solution a   For the Third correct solution a

PRIZE OF $25 ❧ PRIZE OF $10

all payable in STANDARD LINE type at list prices. It should be borne in mind that STANDARD LINE at list prices is worth more than the ordinary type at 50 per cent off. ☛ ☛ Solutions should be addressed to "Prize Contest, Inland Type Foundry, St. Louis." The correct solution and the names of the prize winners will be duly published in this journal.

Standard prize that, necessary an study depend from of Standard production Standard a briefly Standard and system line, had to find rule, with of well is on range Leaders with worth verdict before. All series filling course printer. All Standard Line matter profitable to prominent printer. For it is the type to satisfy every quick and economic printer as the best. Standard Line is the greatest system. We view it as the one sufficient for practical or progressive printing. Profits are now numerous with this Line and the type is well appreciated. No printer will question the fact that the points of special excellence quickly and thoroughly commend the new type, and perhaps require no further additional dissertation to readily declare the usefulness of it. The gratification becomes wider by extending purchase of faces cast upon the simple Line used for plain or other material. Another point any one may pause on to be considered, and a feature to be mentioned: Leaders line accurately with every face and body; the setting in position by compositor is subject to any requirement and will do it justice; justification in combination on any body, If point leads or slugs alone be the means The feature in legal blanks of 2-Point faces in brass we offer as justified in every typographic specimen. When all have the entire fancy printing outfit, their sizes of all leaders will Line accurately All single letter- itself cast to line by any other shown classes the caps of any one body are on same Line will line other as small caps, also leaders a any a bill bodies, be but be body be body can cast could can date- dotted, ever few events far face had heads hence have it in line leads lengthy lines lead means may of of on of of on or of of of point Rome. rest roads slugs. so than this the this that thus that time that them upon will what would what would will

INLAND TYPE FOUNDRY

Inventors and Manufacturers of
STANDARD LINE TYPE ☛   217-219 Olive Street, SAINT LOUIS

This page, excepting the Pi, is set in our KELMSCOTT Series. Borders No. 1833 and 1850; latter around page.

The contest alluded to in this advertisement from the Inland Type Foundry in the Inland Printer (7:5, August, 1896, p. 571) provided the company a most effective means of demonstrating its newly introduced lining system. Before the system, a lining form such as this would have been virtually impossible to compose.

In that speech, Werner noted he had met Nelson C. Hawks on two occasions. "We congratulated one-another—him for the success of the point system, me for the success of the standardized type-face alignment.[12]

The well-conceived plan adopted by Inland Type Foundry created three standard alignments. The great bulk of the type manufactured was of precisely the same alignment. Shoulders were sized by multiples of whole points, facilitating the alignment of different body sizes with one- or two-point leads. A second alignment was for *title* lettering, where no lowercase or descending characters were used. These faces filled the body, with only a small shoulder at the bottom; this shoulder also was sized to the even point. Finally, a *standard script line* was created for faces with descenders of unusual length which would kern excessively if cast on standard lines. Alignment, again, was to the even point.

All type manufactured by Inland Type Foundry, regardless of size, could be aligned perfectly with leads, and so, for the first time, there was no need for pieces of paper and cardboard spacing in the printshop.

American Type Founders eventually adopted this concept, coming out with the first point line specimen book in 1902.[13]

It is noted that the standard line established only common base lines for all letters. Today more than ever before, there is great discussion over the fact that point sizes primarily refer to the sizes of the metal bodies; they have no direct relationship to the height of the letters on

[12] Ibid.

[13] *American Line Type Faces* (Jersey City, N. J.: American Type Founders Company, 1902).

those metal bodies as measured from the tallest ascender to the deepest descender. Some designs employ the entire body; others have a point or two of "built-in" white space.

Point-Set Bodies

Nelson Hawks did not abandon his point system after seeing the idea adopted by many founders. Watching the system evolve, he took note of continuing complaints about the set width of bodies which had been totally unrestricted. The typefounder often found it difficult to determine precisely which set was used on a given letter. As one author noted:

> At present there is no certainty that extra sorts will correspond in width with the original fonts; it is scarcely possible that they should. My dealings have been with the best houses, and I find the difficulty of obtaining extras to match the original set is very great. . . .
>
> I know just where the oppostiion will chiefly come—not so much from the founder as from the designer. It is so nice and easy to jot down a design in freehand fashion, with sprawling limbs and curly tails, and it certainly takes more trouble to do as the great master of type design did—make every part conform to some regular scale. . . ."[14]

Complaints such as this inspired Hawks to recommend fixed sets based on point units. As he explained later:

> The value of the point should not be confined to bodies alone. The widths also should be considered. For numerous and arbitrary widths in such a roman font we are indebted to the caprice of the punch cutter or designer. In some cases there are 70 or more widths, which very easily could be

---

[14]R. Coupland Harding, "Lining and Set of Type," *Inland Printer,* 14:2 (November, 1894), 131.

_& Pt. 10 on_
Hawks system

Chicago and Northwestern Railroad
now running into the wild and wicked
western country where Indians are on
the war path for red headed scalps.
In the language of the poet and when
we are invited to go out and take the
bull by the horns it behooves a man to
hustle and make hay while the wind
blows through his galways Santa Anna
I wish Miner would stick that bill of
Ben Butler is in Chicago at present.
Cleveland And Stevenson are all right.
We.are net in it "in what" the syndi
"Celebrated Superior Copper Mixed"
How about the COMET in Chicago it
:: Come'th not. Northern Pacific R. R

This is proof of first type set on Point
widths, + mailed to me in New York by
Barnhart Bros. Chicago, who cast this
type at my suggestion. The writing above
is Barnhart's and is testimony of my
authority as originator of the widths. ___ _NCH_

First proof of point-set types from the Barnhart Brothers and Spindler
foundry in Chicago. Inscription by Hawks explains Barnhart's penned
note. From the Kemble Collections.

reduced to 10 or less, and each width a definite number of points, and by using point spaces perfect spacing would result, with a saving of time. I brought this matter up to Barnhart Brothers in Chicago in 1892, and they tried it out successfully.[15]

The Barnhart Brothers & Spindler foundry adopted the point set idea before adopting the lining system. "Soon after the adoption of the Point Body System," the company explained in its *Specimen Book No. 9,* "we inaugurated a self-justifying system of cast type faces, which was introduced to the public as Point-Set; naturally when we established our lining system we added to the iteration, Point Body, Point Set, Point Line."[16]

Werner credited Hawks with the idea in the St. Louis speech already mentioned. However, he noted that later on, too much refinement was added to it "when they got to measuring by eighths of a point. This nullified its value in spacing, even though it was good foundry practice in making type casters adhere to a prescribed width (or set), which in earlier days was much neglected."[17]

Kerning Characters

One other complaint of printers regarded kerning f and j characters. Both Central and Inland foundries in St. Louis introduced non-kerning characters to all their fonts and subsequently eliminated f ligatures.[18] This practice was not carried through by other founders;

---

[15]Nelson C. Hawks, "The Point System, Ancient and Modern," *Inland Printer,* 44:3 (December, 1923), 467.

[16]"Point-Line, Point-Set, Point-Body, A Perfect Lining System," *Book of Type Specimens* (Chicago: Barnhart Brothers & Spindler, Specimen Book No. 9, c. 1909), 3.

[17]N. J. Werner, address, op. cit.

[18]Ibid.

ligatures persist even today as do the kerning letters which made them necessary.

Refinements added by Barnhart Brothers and Spindler in Chicago, and the Inland Type Foundry in St. Louis, helped Marder, Luse and Company bring type-founding to measured perfection. What once was a free-wheeling type body, having no precise height, width, depth, or letter position, became a body cast to a precise height-to-paper, a precise point body, a precise point alignment, and a precise point set. Standardization in the American typefounding industry became a frenzied rush toward total implementation. Although old bodies of several configurations still were much in evidence by 1892 when American Type Founders Company was formed, the trend toward standardization was well-established and irreversible.

Chapter Eight

British Adoption of Point System

AT THE OUTSET of this text, it was noted that no standard for manufacturing type existed in the English-speaking world. Matters relating to a standard did not stand still in England while American founders created and adopted their own; yet competition among various founders in England did prevent standardization until after the turn of the present century.

Standards existed for Pica from the 1770's, as noted in various early texts on printing. In those times, the Caslon foundry had a Pica which fit 71.5 to the foot. This standard was adopted by at least one other founder, Miller and Richard.[1] The Caslon foundry changed its standard sometime between 1825 and 1841 so that exactly 72 Picas fit the foot.[2] Known as H. W. Caslon and Company, Ltd., near the turn of the century, the firm watched the American transition with great interest, and advocated British adoption of the American system as early as 1886,[3] the same year the Pica was settled upon by the U. S. Type Founders' Association. The Caslon foundry was somewhat ahead of its time, however. This more

---

[1]"Touching Up the Type Founders," *British & Colonial Printer, & Stationer,* 31:3 (January 19, 1893), 1. Quotation comes from section authored by John Marder.

[2]Ibid.

[3]"The Point System—Which Standard" *British Printer,* 14:81 (May-June, 1901), 117.

conservative comment was made by James Figgins of the
V. & J. Figgins type foundry:

> The latest scare ... is the desire expressed by a few
> printers to again upset all the existing 'standards' and type
> bodies that have taken sixty years to establish and consolidate,
> and to substitute the American Bodies, none of which coin-
> cide with those now in general use; the system, in fact, has all
> the disadvantages of the Didot Point, the unit is too large, and
> while the result is scarcely in harmony with any of the existing
> standards it fails entirely to provide for many necessary
> bodies without quickly relapsing into fractions of points
> which add greatly to the general confusion without any cor-
> responding advantage.[4]

Precisely how the bodies he mentions came about
was something less than scientific. One founder of that
era, a Henry Rush, suggested that printers themselves
were principally responsible for anomalities in bodies.

> Even early in the present century [19th] type was not kept
> in stock by the typefounders, but cast to order, the large
> printers supplying their own ems for patterns. Some of these
> were English and some foreign, consequently, variations in
> bodies owe their origin and perpetuation to the printers. The
> accommodating, amiable, and obliging typefounder cast just
> what he was asked for by his various customers, altering his
> moulds to suit their patterns and supplying other printers
> from any surplus stock. In fact, the foundry I am connected
> with keeps two sizes of Long Primer in stock, one standard
> and the other called *Austin's* body; two Breviers, one standard
> and the other called *Nichol's* body; which necessarily means
> extra expense and inconvenience to typefounders.[5]

---

[4]Ibid.

[5]Henry Rush, "Type Bodies," *British Printer*, 3:14 (March-April, 1890), 12.

Type Importation

The fact that the French, Americans and other nationalities had standards was more than of passing interest to printers in Britain. They were importing these types. Some type founders dismissed the idea that printers were importing foreign types in order to get types "on the system." Others made the changeover to "the system" to gain a better trade balance with foreign typefounders. Others, such as quoted here, dismissed the entire idea.

> This Point System, moreover, would not lead, if adopted, to reciprocity of trade with the United States of America, for the high protective tariff in vogue there entirely shuts the door against anything of the kind, and thus, while the system might cause confusion in many offices here, it could have no other effect, except perhaps to raise the prices of type to the much higher American rates, which are very considerably in excess of those charged by the English founders.[6]

This was James Figgins speaking. The Caslon foundry, however, used American importation as a chief reason for adopting the American system:

> . . . But seeing that so much type of American manufacture is now in use in this country, we have adopted it as our standard and shall adhere to it.[7]

The *British Printer,* an active trade publication during that era, concluded that foreign competition came about chiefly because of standardization in those countries.

> Our own experience—we give it for what it is worth—is that the [British] Associated Founders have vastly underrated the extent of German and American competition. We entirely agree with those people who believe that had the home

---

[6]"The Point System . . . " op. cit.
[7]Ibid.

founders shewn their present enterprise some years ago, foreign competition in type would be trifling compared with what it is to-day, when practically every job office possesses more or less material from these sources.[8]

By 1900, nearly all British typefounders had adopted a standard of some sort. There was great argument, however, over the fact that there were different systems. As in the United States, argument centered mostly around *precisely* how large the Pica would be.

Confusion over the size of the Pica was promulgated even by John Marder, whose Chicago foundry initiated the system in 1877. In early chapters both Marder and Nelson Hawks were found to be calling their Pica "one-sixth of an inch." Marder frequently made this statement in his writing and such surely caused consternation on the part of British forerunners of the reform, such as the Caslon foundry.

That foundry had written Marder, Luse and Company regarding its standard, which was stated to be a sixth of an inch. This, Caslon happily noted, accorded with the standard already in use in the foundry. "To make sure of the matter, however, we obtained from the leading firm of American typefounders (now one of the Typefounders' Association) a steel standard identical in measurement to their own. This standard . . . measures minutely less than six Picas to the inch."[9]

Subsequently, the Caslon foundry changed its molds to conform to the American standard. Other founders argued strongly against the smaller Pica.

---

[8]"The Associated British Type Founders," *British Printer,* 16:93 (May-June, 1903), 114.

[9]"The Point System . . ." op. cit.

Size of Pica Argument

Recalling Chapter 6, it is noted that the American Pica was established at .1660 inch; a sixth of an inch comes to .166⅔. The fraction, dropped with the American Pica, caused six Picas to measure .966 inch.

The P. M. Shanks & Sons, Ltd., foundry insisted that "a Pica one-sixth of the Imperial standard inch was likely to best suit the needs of printers, and notwithstanding the many arguments we have read since, we have seen nothing to alter the opinion then formed."[10]

> We have read the articles on Point System standards with great interest. . . . In all of the articles in question it was distinctly pointed out that no system was likely to be satisfactory that did not adopt as its standard six Picas to the inch or 72 to the foot. It is the standard measurement of the empire. Everything else in the printing office is measured by inches—paper, chases, composing sticks, furniture, rules —and why not type? . . . If the typefounders of the country have departed in the course of years from this simple standard, it is surely better when a change is made that they should return to it, than that a bastard standard, however infinitesimal the difference, should be introduced.[11]

Others were as strongly in favor of a point measuring .1660. Foremost among the latter was Walter Haddon, who traded as John Haddon & Company. He led a strenuous campaign on the subject, gave many lectures concerning it, and started a typefoundry to produce types and composing room material made entirely to the point system measurement of .1660 inch to the Pica.[12]

---

[10]"Adoption of the Point System," *British Printer,* 16:95 (September-October, 1903) 258.

[11]"The Point System . . ." op. cit.

[12]R. C. Elliot, "The Development of the 'Point' Unit of Type Measurement," *The Monotype Recorder,* 30:241 (1931), 16.

Advocates of the American Pica concluded that those opposing the American standard were "trifling with customers." Because their Picas were so close to the new standard, opponents could see no real need for alteration.

Nevertheless, one-by-one, founders fell into line. The Shanks foundry, already quoted, made this snide remark:

> When finally deciding to cast the whole of our bodies on the Point System (American standard), we addressed enquiries to a number of eminent printers who had been using our type in conjunction with American . . . as to whether any difficulty had been experienced in working our then existing point bodies with those supplied from the other side, and the unanimous answer was that they found no difficulty whatever, and until our enquiry were not aware that a difference even existed. . . ."[13]

L. B. Benton, then manager of the American Type Founders Company, also minimized the differences by noting "that type increases in size when in actual use by the accumulation of foreign substances,"[14] and that in actual use, the smaller American bodies soon were as large as British bodies direct from the foundry.

Demanded, nevertheless, was a single standard. British founders eventually fell into line behind the American standard.

The American and British inches differ by one three-hundred thousandth. This therefore would cause miniscule differences between the two point systems, according to the logic of H. H. Taylor, principal of

---

[13]"The Point System . . ." op. cit., 118.
[14]Ibid., 116.

Taylor & Taylor, a firm which pioneered fine printing in San Francisco in the earlier years of this century.[15] For precise accuracy, therefore, it is important to discover how British typefounders obtained their standards.

As already stated, the H. W. Caslon firm obtained its standards from "the leading firm of American typefounders." This most likely was the MacKellar, Smiths and Jordan foundry, whose Pica was specifically selected in 1886 as *the* standard for the American typefounding industry.

In 1903, to check whether a true standard existed among members of the British Type Founders Association, *The British Printer* obtained standards from the "Associated Type Founders of America" (perhaps ATF) to use in checking against the standards used in British foundries. At the time, only three founders comprised the British association: H. W. Caslon & Company, Miller and Richard, and Stepehnson, Blake & Company. The magazine's visit to the three foundries and on-site comparison of standards revealed precise agreement. At the Stephenson, Blake foundry, a further comparison was made.

> . . . Two of the hardened steel standards actually in use for testing purposes were measured by micrometer in our presence and compared with the pattern standards received from Messrs. MacKellar, Smiths & Jordan in 1898, with the result that perfect agreement was demonstrated. . . .[16]

Thus, it is concluded that British typefounders made no interpretation of the American standard. Rather, they made every effort to cast their types precisely to the

---

[15]H. H. Taylor, personal letter to Beatrice Warde, Dec. 24, 1931.

[16]"The Associated British Type Founders," op. cit., 113.

hardened steel standards actually provided to them by American foundries. Miniscule differences between American and British inches had no opportunity to creep into the system.

In addition to the three members of the British Typefounders Association, *The British Printer* reported late in 1903 that the Caxton Type Foundry (John Haddon & Company), Sir Charles Reed & Sons, Ltd., P. M. Shanks & Sons, Ltd., and the Wicks Rotary Type-Casting Company, Ltd., all had undertaken to *guarantee* supplies on the recognized bodies.[17]

Condescending to the new standard, the Shanks foundry noted:

> Without . . . arousing fresh controversy, we will content ourselves with saying we have accepted the decision arrived at and have completed our arrangements for supplying on the American standard of .166044 of an inch, and like other British foundries have forfeited the accuracy of the gauges made by ourselves by obtaining others from a leading American foundry.[18]

Point Line and Point Set

Due to the lateness in adopting the American system, most British foundries were able to adopt concepts of point set and point line simultaneously. As noted by the *London Times* when reviewing accomplishments of the Stephenson, Blake foundry in 1911:

> What is called the "American Point System," which originally was understood as referring merely to a systematic regulation of the size of type bodies with reference to a definite numerical standard, has aroused much interest, and

---

[17]"Adoption of the Point System," op. cit.
[18]Ibid.

has since been extended so as to govern also the position of type on the body as regards alignment, as well as still more recently the thickness of the types. In its entirety the system is known as the "point body line and set system." In the Sheffield foundry, although the firm did not nominally begin to cast on American point bodies till the end of 1897, preparations had to be made for that event for a number of years, and finally the system was adopted in its entirety with a thoroughness unequalled on this side of the Atlantic.[19]

Point line generally was accepted from the outset. Point set was adopted more slowly.

Thus, the final chapter in standardization of printing types in the English-speaking world was completed. Even though type itself today has become an outmoded and peculiar thing, especially in the United States, the relative newness of the American point system is attested to by the fact that nearly all collectors of old printing types, whether hobbyist or devoted professional, can boast of items in their collections which do not fit the point system.

It's curious to note an idea as far-sweeping as a standard measurement is yet to be 100 years old. It also is curious to note that, until now, details of its introduction, spread and adoption have been obscured by tales and superstition. Hopefully, the *real* story is now known.

---

[19]"Type Founding. A Record of Mechanical Progress," *London Times,* November 22, 1911, p. 16, Engineering Supplement.

The First Announcement?

Although it has no integral marking for positive identification, the leaf reproduced on the opposite page very well may be the first printed announcement of the point system, issued in San Francisco by Nelson Hawks in 1879.

The sheet comes from the private collection of Roger Levenson of Berkeley, California, who, upon researching the subject a few years ago noted "to judge from the wording, it appears to have been a preliminary to the formal announcement that was printed in the 1879 winter issue of The Chicago Specimen." *The existence of this leaf is alluded to in Chapter 4, page 31, and was brought to the author's attention when Mr. Levenson reviewed proofs of this book's text.*

PROGRESS OF AMERICAN TYPE FOUNDING !

Marder, Luse & Company's Emancipation Proclamation to the Printers of the World, of the Abolition of Irregular Type Bodies! Mammoth Undertaking for the advancement of the Art Preservative! Perfection at last!

EXPLANATION OF

THOSE **NEW** BODIES

EVERY printer, of any experience, knows the misery of a mixture of type bodies in an office. No perfect system of justification exists in this country, nor in Great Britain; every foundry varying, more or less, from the others, and the gradation of sizes being irregular with all of them.

Our firm have resolved, cost what it may, to come to the rescue ; and for a year and nine months past the good work has been in progress. We are shouldering this enormous and expensive undertaking without aid ; believing that we shall receive from all printers a full appreciation and reward in due course of time.

To illustrate this system, we show a Table of Sizes, and their Proportion to each other by twelfths of Pica, our present Pica being the standard.

1 American,	5 Pearl,	12 PICA,
1½ German,	5½ Agate,	14 English,
2 Saxon,	6 NONPAREIL,	16 Columbian.
2½ Norse,	7 Minion,	18 Great Primer,
3 Brilliant,	8 Brevier,	20 Paragon,
3½ Ruby,	9 Bourgeois,	22 Double Small Pica,
4 Excelsior,	10 Long Primer,	24 Double Pica,
4½ Diamond,	11 Small Pica,	28 Double English, etc.

American	German	Saxon	Norse	Brilliant	Ruby	Excelsior	Diamond	Pearl	Agate	Nonpareil	Minion	Brevier	Bourgeois	Long Primer	Small Pica	Pica
1	1½	2	2½	3	3½	4	4½	5	5½	6	7	8	9	10	11	12

Each size is a factor. Three Nonpareils are a Great Primer ; three Breviers are a Double Pica ; a Nonpareil and a Brevier are an English, or Two-line Minion. That odd body, Bourgeois, is now a respectable size, being a Nonpareil-and-a-half exactly. Look over the figures, and you will understand how beautifully simple job composition will be in an office fitted up with MARDER, LUSE & COMPANY'S type!

Type of the same series are cast to the same *line;* so that the different sizes are quickly and perfectly justified, without resorting to cardboard, paper, &c.

SOME ADVICE, THAT IT WILL PAY TO TAKE.—Don't hang on to your old material *too long;* but work it off before this new system renders it totally unsaleable! Clean out the old founts, and sell them ; amateurs may be handy customers for you. Begin NOW to get ready for this wonderful change, for it is close upon us.

MARDER, LUSE & CO.

CHICAGO AND SAN FRANCISCO.

Bibliography

As mentioned in the introduction, this book would not have been possible if it were not for the extensive collections of rare house organs, specimen books, trade journals and personal correspondence made available to me at the libraries listed. This makes bibliographic organization most difficult. Those items requiring annotation are first listed. Type specimen books, always a problem in bibliographic lists, also are listed separately.

From Special Collections

Of critical importance to this research was a complete file of both *The Pacific Specimen* and *The Chicago Specimen* in the Kemble Collections at the California Historical Society. The ATF Collection at Columbia University maintains an incomplete file of both journals.

"American System of Interchangeable Type Bodies." Advertisement in *The Chicago Specimen*, 13:3&4 (3d Quarter, 1879), page unnumbered.
> Also appeared in *The Pacific Specimen*, 5:3 (3d Quarter, 1880). Kemble Collections and ATF/Columbia Collections.

Bateman, George W. "Points," *The Superior Printer*, 2:5&6 (September-October, 1888), 5.
> From author's personal collection.

"Caution." *The Pacific Printer, Stationer & Lithographer*, 8:7 (July, 1884), 9.
> Published by Palmer & Rey foundry in San Francisco. Kemble Collections.

"Change in Firm," *The Pacific Specimen*, 6:4 (4th Quarter, 1881), 1.
> Kemble Collections.

"The Fractional System," *Pacific Printer, Stationer & Lithographer*, 7:1 (January, 1883), 10.

"Gossip with Correspondents and Readers," *The Chicago Specimen*, 4:4 (October, 1870), 3-4.
> Kemble Collections. Much of this article was used (with no credit given) in Ringwalt's *Encyclopaedia*. See bibliographic reference.

Hawks, Nelson C., personal journal of sales of his iron bracket composing stand.
> Kemble Collections.

Hawks, Nelson C., personal journal or diary.
> Kemble Collections.

Hawks, N. C., personal letter to H. L. Bullen, August 21, 1912.
> Original letter preserved in ATF-Columbia Collections. Reproduced in Bullen's article on Hawks in *Inland Printer*. See bibliographic reference.

"Hawks's Aliquot System of Bodies," *Pacific Printer, Stationer &
Lithographer*, 8:6 (June, 1884), 11-14.

"Interchangeable Type Bodies," *The Pacific Printer*, 4:3&4 (July,
1880), 2.

> This periodical was labeled "Miller & Richard's Trade Journal published
> by J. J. Palmer, San Francisco" and surely was predecessor of *Pacific Printer,
> Stationer & Lithographer.*

"The Journal's Outfit," *San Mateo* (Calif.) *Journal,* November 27,
1829.

> Clipping was kept in a scrapbook by Hawks, now preserved in the Kemble
> Collections.

"Justification of Type Bodies," *The Chicago Specimen*, 10:1
(January, 1876), 2.

> Kemble Collections.

"Late Specimens," *The Chicago Specimen*, 11:3 (3d Quarter, 1877),
3.

Marder, John. "Touching-Up the Type Founders," *The British &
Colonial Printer & Stationer*, 31:3 (January 19, 1893), 2.

> Single leaf is preserved in the Kemble Collections. Marder's hand-written
> manuscript for this article is preserved in the ATF-Columbia Collections.

Marder, Luse & Company, *Illustrated Type Making with a Descriptive
Article upon the American System of Interchangeable Type Bodies.*

> Pamphlet published around 1880 at Chicago and preserved in the Kem-
> ble Collections.

"Marder, Luse and Company," *Paper and Press*, 6:1 (January,
1888), 22.

> From the author's personal collection.

"Marder, Luse & Company vs. N. C. Hawks."

> Flier published by ML&Co. around 1882-1883, preserved in the Kemble
> Collections.

"New Type Bodies," *The Pacific Specimen*, 4:1 (1st Quarter, 1879),
2.

"O. B. and N. B.," *The Pacific Specimen*, 5:4 (4th Quarter, 1880), 5.

Patton, William M., "Thomas MacKellar," *Official Souvenir, Eighth
Annual Convention of the United Typothetae of America* (1894), 31.

> Kemble Collections.

"The Point System," *Typographic Gazette*, 4:10 (Fall and Winter,
1887-88), 1.

> Published by H. H. Thorp Manufacturing Company, proprietors of the
> C leveland Type Foundry. Kemble Collections.

"The Printer's Friend," *The Neat Printer*, 1:3 (December, 1886), 1.
    Published by the Cranston Press, San Antonio, Texas. Leaf preserved in
    ATF-Columbia Collections.

Proceedings of the Fifteenth Meeting of the Type Founders' Association of the U. S., Held at Spencer House, Niagara Falls, N. Y., September 16, 1886.
    Printed minutes of meeting preserved in pamphlet form in ATF-Columbia Collections.

"Proportions of Type," *The Printers Miscellany*, (published by George Bruce and Company), undated.
    This detached leaf is preserved in the ATF-Columbia Collection.

Proposals for Establishing a Graduated Scale of Sizes for the Bodies of Printing Types . . . 3d Edition, Sheffield: Bower Brothers, 1841.
    Preserved as a pamphlet in the ATF-Columbia Collections.

Taylor, H. H., personal letter to Beatrice Warde, December 24, 1931.
    Carbon copy of letter preserved in the Kemble Collections.

Type Founders' Association of the United States. *Constitution.* Adopted January 20-21, 1864, Astor House, New York City.
    Printed booklet in ATF-Columbia Collections.

"Uniform Type Bodies," *Typographic Advertiser* by MacKellar, Smiths & Jordan Company, Philadelphia, 31:117&118 (Springtime, 1885).
    Kemble Collections.

Untitled printed copy of draft agreement dated February 27, 1882, signed by A. P. Luse and N. C. Hawks in San Jose, California.
    Kemble Collections.

Werner, N. J., "An Address," presented by Werner at a meeting of the St. Louis Club of Printing House Craftsmen.
    Printed booklet with notations in front cover by H. L. Bullen preserved in
    ATF-Columbia Collections. Bullen dates it "after 1928."

Letters received from A. P. Luse by Nelson Hawks during the period are preserved by the Kemble Collections. The following have been used with this text:
March 4, 1876; July 26, 1878; August 24, 1878; August 28, 1878; August 30, 1878; February 24, 1879; May 31, 1879; September 9, 1879; October 3, 1879; November 5, 1879; November 21, 1879; April 30, 1880; July 2, 1880; October 10, 1880; October 28, 1880; January 18, 1881; February 4, 1882.

Three letters from John Marder to Nelson Hawks were used as references. Luse carried on most of the company's correspondence as indicated by the previous list of references.

Undated letter (around 1879); March 8, 1878; February 22, 1882.

Articles

"Adoption of the Point System," *The British Printer*, 16:95 (September-October, 1903), 253.

"American Typefounders Co.," *Inland Printer*, 10:2 (November, 1892), 150.

"American Typefounders Co.," *Inland Printer*, 10:5 (February, 1893), 393-4.

"Answers to Correspondence," *Inland Printer*, 3:12 (September, 1886), 771.

"The Associated British Type Founders," *The British Printer*, 16:93 (May-June 1903), 111-114.

Bishop, H. G. "The Practical Printer," *Inland Printer*, 5:4 (January, 1888), 247.

Bullen, Henry L. "Nelson C. Hawks' 'Invention' of the American Point System," *Inland Printer*, 46:11 (August, 1929), 65-66.

Eckman, James. "The Chicago Type Foundry of Marder, Luse & Company, 1863-1892," *Printing and Graphic Arts*, 7:3 (September, 1959), 77.

———. "The Great Western Type Foundry of Barnhart Brothers & Spindler, 1869-1933," *Printing and Graphic Arts* 9:1 (March 1961), 10.

Elliott, R. C. "The Development of the 'Point' Unit of Type Measurement," *The Monotype Recorder*, 30:241 (1931), 15.

Harding, R. Coupland. "Lining and Set of Type," *Inland Printer*, 14:2 (November, 1894), 131.

Hawks, Nelson C. "How the Point System Was Started," *Printing Art*, 36:5 (January, 1921), 389.

———. "The Point System, Ancient and Modern," *Inland Printer*, 44:3 (December, 1923), 467-68.

Loy, William E. "Typefounders and Typefounding in America, No. XXVII—Nelson Crocker Hawks," *Inland Printer*, 23:2 (November, 1902), 249.

Murdock, Charles A. "History of Printing in San Francisco," *Pacific Printer & Publisher*, 33:4 (April, 1925), 278-279.

"Nelson C. Hawks" (obituary), *The Pacific Printer*, 42:1 (July, 1929), 53.

"Patents of Interest," *Inland Printer*, 3:10 (July, 1886), 626.

"The Point System—Which Standard?" *The British Printer*, 14:81 (May-June, 1901), 115-118.

Rush, Henry. "Type Bodies," *The British Printer, Stationery & Fancy Trades Gazette*, 3:14 (March-April, 1890), 9-12.

"Sensible Suggestions," *Inland Printer*, 5:9 (June, 1888), 676.

Smalian, Felix. "Who Discovered and Perfected the French Typographical Point?" *Inland Printer*, 70:5 (February, 1923), 672.

"Special Announcement American Typefounders' Company." *Inland Printer*, 10:5 (February, 1893), 399.

"Standard Measurement," *Inland Printer*, 2:3 (December, 1884), 110.

"Standard Measurement," *Inland Printer*, 2:5 (February, 1885), 211.

"35% Discount" (advertisement), *Inland Printer*, 6:8 (May, 1889), 702.

Tracy, Walter. "The Point," *The Penrose Annual*, LV (1961), 63.

"Trade Notes," *Inland Printer*, 12:6 (March, 1894), 508.

"Type Bodies," *The British Printer, Stationery and Fancy Trades Gazette*, 3:14 (March-April, 1890), 11.

"Type Founding. A Record of Mechanical Progress," *London Times*, November 22, 1911, page 16 of Engineering Supplement.

"Uniformity in Type Bodies," *Inland Printer*, 8:1 (October, 1890), 71-73.

Werner, N. J., Postscript to "Who Discovered and Perfected French Typographical Point System?" by Felix Smalian, *Inland Printer*, 70:5 (February, 1923), 672.

"A Word to Type-founders," *Inland Printer*, 2:6 (April, 1885), 305.

Books

DeVinne, Theodore L. *The Practice of Typography: A Treatise on the Process of Type-Making, the Point System, the Names, Sizes, Styles and Prices of Plain Printing Types.* 2d ed. New York: The Century Press, 1902.

Johnson, J. *Typographica, or the Printers' Instructor.* Vol. II, London: Longman, Hurst, Rees, Orme, Brown and Green, 1824.

Legros, Lucien A. and Grant, John C. *Typographical Printing Surfaces.* London: Longman, Green, and Company, 1916.

Mergenthaler Linotype Company. *Useful Matrix Information.* Brooklyn, N. Y.: 1937.

Moxon, Joseph. *Mechanick Exercises: Or, the Doctrine of Handy-Works Applied to the Art of Printing.* Vol. II, London: Printed for Joseph Moxon at the West Side of Fleet Ditch at the Sign of Atlas, 1683.

Ringwalt, J. Luther, ed. *American Encyclopaedia of Printing.* Philadelphia: Menamin & Ringwalt, 1871.

Foundry Specimen Books

American Line Type Faces. Jersey City, N. J.: American Type Founders Company, 1902.

Hawks & Shattuck's New Specimen Book. San Francisco: Hawks & Shattuck, 1889.

Improved Type for Printers. St. Louis: Inland Type Foundry, 1895.

Price List of Type and Printing Material. St. Louis: Central Type Foundry, July, 1890.

Book of Type Specimens. Chicago: Barnhart Brothers & Spindler, Specimen Book No. 9, c. 1909.

Specimen of Printing Types from the Letter Foundry of James Ronaldson, Successor to Binny & Ronaldson. Philadelphia: James Ronaldson, 1822.

Specimens of Printing Types Made at Bruce's New York Type-Foundry. New York: George Bruce's Son & Company, 1882.

Price List of Type and Printing Material. St. Louis: Central Type Foundry, 1886.

Index

Colophon

"Hand-set" by the author and produced in Baskerville on a Mergenthaler VIP phototypesetter. "Hand-set" refers to detailed keying of mortises wherever appropriate plus the inclusion of ligatures as available from Mergenthaler. Printed offset on 60-pound Warren Olde Style. All production done at the Pioneer Press of West Virginia, Inc., Terra Alta, W. Va. 26764, of which the author is a principal officer.